op

650

salt
the
mysterious
necessity

Edited by MARK BATTERSON and WILLIAM W. BODDIE

Designer: Ed Brun

Photography: *Cover, Howard Garrett; Page 6, Magnum; Page 12, Black Star; Page 30, Black Star; Page 34, Emil Schulthess; Pages 40-41, Comet; Page 52, Comet; Pages 59, 61, 63, 64, 65, Dr. Georg Gerster; Page 66, Black Star; Page 74, Comet; Page 84, Black Star; Pages 88-89, 92-93, 94, 95, 96, 97, 98, Dr. Georg Gerster; Pages 100, 104, 105, Dr. Georg Gerster.*

Cover: *The plain white salt crystal takes on color and beauty when viewed by a microscope. In much the same way, when viewed in historical perspective, "common" salt is found to have had major impact upon man and his civilizations.*

contents

Introduction

A wise man once said that there is a built-in irony to almost everything in life.

He might have added, in elaboration, that there is also irony in the fact that in spite of what history tries to teach us time and again, we are still generally unable to perceive the ironic aspects of situations while they are still affecting us, but only after the fact.

That is certainly the case with salt, which is what this volume — "Salt, the Mysterious Necessity"—is all about.

There is no question that from the beginning of the human race, salt has indeed been both mysterious and necessary to man, as well as to every other member of the animal world. The irony here is that while it has been used to meet some very basic necessities, man has been able to unlock many of the mysteries of salt only during the past couple of centuries. It is the unraveling of these mysteries that has led to progress beyond the ken of such adventurers as Christopher Columbus and Ferdinand Magellan, both of whom had destinies which were inextricably linked with salt, and who both played their roles in life with unusual verve and imagination.

As various segments of this work make clear, man has needed common salt (sodium chloride) to help maintain a certain balance in his own personal internal sea. It is necessary to his life. He has also used salt to help remove the shackles imposed by his birthplace. It has influenced his travels and explorations around the world. For without a source of salt to draw upon to preserve foodstuffs, he would not have been able to wander so widely and to explore and to learn and ultimately, to progress to his present state of being.

What all of this means, in fact, is that salt has really been far more important to the lifeblood and progress of man than have the more glamorous treasures such as gold. Hindsight makes it obvious that the alchemists of the Middle Ages would have been better advised to have spent more effort in trying to unlock the many mysteries of salt than they were to spend so much time in their attempts to make gold. They might well have succeeded at least in part in the former; they certainly failed in the latter.

It took four men—Nicolas Leblanc, a French physician; Albert and Ernest Solvay, Belgian brothers who became interested in industrial salt chemistry; and Herbert H. Dow, an American who became interested in brine during his senior year at college—to expand our knowledge of salt so that our world became a far different and better place in which to live in the span of just a few decades.

Salt has been strongly linked to adventure and to adventurers. It has been the focal point of major expeditions, the underlying cause of various wars, and the ultimate prize of many an excruciating endeavor. Countless men, women and children have died over it, but far more have managed to enhance the progress of themselves and their descendants because of their acquisition and realistic use of it. It has stirred the imagination and talents of scientists and thus has led to the betterment of life on earth.

It is in these facts that we again find an irony. For it took man many thousands of years to appreciate that the most exhilarating adventures of all can be mental, rather than physical. Often, the trail of salt was essentially physical, fascinating though it has always been. But the most magnificent adventures related to salt have been in the minds of men such as Herbert H. Dow, a soft spoken, studious chemist who calmly but with utmost determination went his way—and founded what was to become one of the most innovative and useful organizations in the history of man through his adventurous use of salt.

This work was started several years ago. In all frankness, we didn't realize what we were getting into at the beginning. It was just that a number of people in the United States and Europe—including Zoltan Merszei, the president of Dow Chemical Europe S.A.; C. M. Doscher, vice president for Marketing for Dow Europe; Dr. Georg Gerster, a Swiss photographer and writer; W. W. Boddie, a Dow consultant who has always been fascinated by history; and I—became interested in exploring the heritage of Dow. As we dug more deeply into the subject of salt, we realized that there should be no turning back. It became obvious that one of the most fascinating subjects in the development of man and his civilization had never been truly written in this context. Just as obviously, the magnificent intellectual adventures of men such as Leblanc, the Solvay brothers, and Dow had never been properly related to the heritage from which we all stem.

From that beginning, others within the organization of The Dow Chemical Company, which has become one of the real industrial movers of the world as the result of its expansion of the capabilities of salt, became equally fascinated with the subject. These men included

C. B. Branch, president of Dow; Earle B. Barnes, president of Dow Chemical U.S.A.; H. D. Doan, president of Dow at the time this project was started and a grandson of the founder; Herbert H. Dow, member of Dow's board of directors and also a grandson of the founder; Dr. Julius E. Johnson, Dow's director of Research and Life Sciences; Dr. A. P. Beutel, long time Dow board member until his retirement in 1971; and Nelson D. Griswold, also a retired member of Dow's board of directors.

When all was said and done, three men were primarily responsible for the results that follow. These were Boddie, Dr. Gerster, and the science writer, Lawrence Galton.

In keeping with the theme, it is perhaps interesting and certainly appropriate that all three men happen to be something more than talented writers or photographers. They are also adventurers.

Boddie, who wrote all of the historical segments, is a South Carolinian who left his birthplace to become a correspondent for *Newsweek* magazine in the South Pacific during World War II. He later served as chief of *Newsweek's* Rome bureau, and eventually became director of public relations for Dow's Texas Division and other Gulf Coast operations. He is now director of the Historical Research Foundation of Lake Jackson, Texas.

Dr. Gerster travels the world on a wide variety of assignments for *National Geographic* magazine as well as for other publications. His adventures as photographer in connection with this particular work on salt carried him to the Imperial Valley of California, the "floating gardens" of the Aztecs near Mexico City, and into the far reaches of Ethiopia.

Galton is a prolific writer who also travels the world. His trail generally ends in one hospital or another for the compilation of material which has made him one of the world's leading writers on subjects relating to the world of medicine.

What follows, then, is the result of their work. If it serves to help us better understand some of the mysteries that have surrounded salt and to relate much of the heritage that belongs to all of us in general and to Dow in particular, their travels and thoughts will have been more than worthwhile.

Some of the great relationships and influences which salt has exerted upon civilization will become obvious to readers of these pages.

—*Mark Batterson*

Man's Internal Sea

Man's internal sea is a salty one. Whether he lives or dies—and how well he lives—depends very much on the salt he must constantly use and have renewed within him.

Because, there, the first primitive forms originated, the ocean has been the mother of life. And even as life moved to the land, it had to take the sea with it. In man and every land animal, the sea is present in the form of fluids and dissolved salts within the armor of the skin.

It has to be.

Where the ocean could stream back and forth through the bodies of primitive water creatures, in land animals an internal sea must circulate to accomplish the same purposes: to bathe all cells, to nourish them, to remove their wastes, and, as it is now known, to do much more.

Of man's total body weight, fluids make up 70 percent, with 5 percent being accounted for by plasma, the fluid carrier of blood cells. There is the interstitial fluid, present between the blood vessel system and the tissue cells, which accounts for 15 percent. And the intracellular fluid, the liquid within cells themselves, makes up half of body weight.

In this internal sea, salt is a vital constituent. The fact that its concentration in the extracellular fluids—both the interstitial and the plasma—is like that of salt in sea water is a reminder of man's marine ancestry. The salt in the human body is enough to fill several salt shakers.

Salt, of course, is sodium chloride. When dissolved in fluid, it forms sodium and chloride, which are electrolytes, so-called because they have electrical charges which allow them to carry current.

Sodium and chloride are the principal electrolytes in interstitial fluid. About 90 percent of the total basic electrolytes in the blood are sodium.

Facing page: A body salt content fascinatingly similar to that of the oceans characterizes man— the highest of the life forms to evolve from all the millions which originated in the earth's great seas.

Sodium is required for muscle contraction. Even the rhythmic beating of the heart depends upon a proper balance of sodium with other minerals, potassium and calcium.

The movement of sodium in and out of nerve fibers is involved in the triggering of nerve impulses.

Sodium also must be present for the digestion of proteins—and it is the chloride from salt which forms hydrochloric acid, a small but essential part of the digestive fluid in the stomach.

And salt has still more functions.

Just as we can work properly only when external conditions are suitable, so the organs of the body work satisfactorily only when internal conditions are constant. So the body seeks to keep those conditions constant. If, for example, we become overheated, we sweat—and the sweat helps to reduce the excessive heat. Salt is a major component of sweat.

One of the most important conditions that must be held constant is the pH of body fluids. pH is a useful way of talking about acidity and alkalinity. One everyday example of the importance of pH is an automobile battery with its series of metal plates dipping into a solution of acid. The battery works properly only at one pH. If water evaporates and acid is left behind, the solution becomes stronger, its pH changes, the generation of electricity becomes less effective, and the battery may be damaged by the strong acid.

Body fluids normally tend to be just slightly alkaline, with a pH value of 7.35 to 7.45. Sodium plays a part in maintaining the pH within that narrow alkalinity range.

Sodium is a component of tears, of saliva, of breast milk, even of semen and prostatic secretions.

One of salt's most critical functions is to regulate the vital exchange of water between the cells and the surrounding fluid. That exchange is made possible by osmosis.

Osmosis is a process you probably encountered in high school biology.

You may recall experiments in which you were given two solutions—one containing water, the other water plus salt—separated from each other by a membrane through which only water could pass. And you saw that a greater amount of water molecules passed from the pure water solution to the salt-plus-water solution than in the reverse direction—until both solutions had the same amount of water molecules.

Such shifting of fluid from one compartment across a membrane to a compartment of lower fluid concentration is osmosis. It depends upon a force, called osmotic pressure, exerted by the sodium and chloride in the salt solution to draw water molecules across the membrane from the pure water solution.

In the body, the wall of a cell is a membrane. And what happens to the water content of the cell depends upon osmotic pressure which, in turn, depends upon the content of sodium in extracellular fluid.

When the salt content of extracellular fluid decreases, osmotic pressure decreases and water moves into the cell. When the salt content of extracellular fluid increases so that osmotic pressure increases, water is transferred out of the cell.

So salt is a vital factor in maintaining a proper balance of water between the cells and their surroundings, without which life would be threatened.

Moreover, salt helps govern thirst which sees to it that enough water is taken in to meet all needs.

Ordinarily, with rest, in moderate climate, without fever and without much perspiration, a person's total water intake per day amounts to about 2½ quarts, with 1½ quarts coming in as liquid and 1 quart obtained from food (including three-tenths of a quart of water produced as proteins, fats and carbohydrates are broken down in the body).

Under normal conditions, the liquid intake is controlled very closely by thirst to meet the actual water requirements of the body. The sensation of thirst depends upon various factors such as the water content of the cells, which in turn is dependent on the concentration of sodium and chloride in the extracellular water.

And the body has remarkable controls to make certain it has all the salt it needs—exactly the right amount, no more and no less.

Intake of salt in the diet varies widely. It appears that two grams worth a day, about 7/100 of an ounce, may represent the minimum daily requirement. But intake may range to as much as 15 grams a day. The ingested salt comes not only from what is added to food at table but also what is present naturally in many meats and other food items.

One day a person may have food which is very salty; the next day, food almost without salt, depending on the whim of a cook.

No matter: The kidney makes certain body salt content holds steady.

The kidney determines what is to be excreted in the urine. As blood flows through the kidney to be purified, that remarkable organ chooses from among the many substances in the blood those to be flushed out and those not to be. It directs all of some, such as proteins, back into the blood. Others, including foreign materials such as drugs, it sends almost entirely into the urine.

Between the extremes—no removal or complete removal—the kidney excretes other constituents into the urine in variable amounts. And this is true of salt.

Within normal bounds, no matter how much or little salt is taken into the body, the salt concentration in the blood and the total amount in the body do not vary. If virtually no salt is taken in, no salt will be excreted; if much salt is absorbed, the excretion rate by the kidney is increased.

Actually, how the kidney handles salt is controlled from a distance. Several powerful hormones from the endocrine glands, especially an adrenal gland hormone called aldosterone which stimulates the reabsorption of sodium and chloride, regulate the work of the kidney cells.

Even as it determines what happens to salt, the kidney determines what happens to water. For every movement of salt in the body brings about movement of water. And, when the kidney sends salt back into the blood, it also sends back water.

Thus, the kidney is no mere body waste removing organ; through its action on salt and other precious materials, it is a guardian of the internal sea and of life-essential chemical balance.

Sometimes, of course, salt balance is upset.

With exposure to the sun or other source of high temperature, the overheated body perspires heavily to reestablish its normal temperature. Excessive sweating removes large quantities of salt as well as fluid. Sweat may initially contain in each quart almost half the usual daily intake of salt. Nevertheless, over a period of time, even though sweating may rise to as much as a quart an hour and even though the amount of salt taken in is not increased, the body acclimatizes itself. There is a sharp fall-off of salt loss; much less salt appears in the sweat and in the urine.

But, for the short term, heavy perspiration can lead to dehydration and heat exhaustion.

Among the first symptoms are headache, a feeling of weakness and dizziness, and nausea. Cramps may also develop in the muscles of arms, legs or abdomen. Later, the victim may turn pale, perspire heavily, and the pulse and breathing rate may shoot up.

Water alone is not enough to establish equilibrium. If water alone is taken, it may be rapidly wasted since perspiration is increased by drinking and that may mean that more salt is lost, only intensifying the problem.

But when salt is taken with the fluid—commonly, half a teaspoonful in a large glass of water or tomato juice is used in emergencies and repeated 3 or 4 times at 10 minute intervals—the salt content of the body is replenished and the salt helps retain water for rehydration.

Because of the efficient conservation of salt by the normal kidney, a salt deficiency virtually never develops as the result of low salt intake alone. But the kidney, as the result of disease or drugs, may fail to conserve salt in normal amounts. A disorder of the adrenal glands may allow kidney wastage of salt. And it is possible for diarrhea, when it is severe, to produce salt deficiency.

In such situations, physicians hasten to prescribe salt-containing solutions to overcome the salt deficit while they seek to find and correct the underlying problem that produced it.

An upset in salt balance, this time on the salt-retention side, may be involved in high blood pressure, or hypertension, a common disorder estimated to affect 20 million people in the United States.

And where once physicians could do little more than restrict salt intake in such cases, which meant great hardship for patients, now they have other means.

That salt might be involved in hypertension was shown by some relatively simple observations. For example, if people with a tendency toward hypertension received an injection of salt solution, their blood pressure rose further.

It was then necessary to study the body's salt controls. And when it was discovered that in people with damage to the adrenal glands atop the kidneys blood pressure fell to abnormally low levels and abnormal amounts of salt were lost, it became clear that the adrenal gland hormones helped to regulate the handling of salt.

With this to go on, it was natural for doctors, faced with patients with the most severe forms of hypertension, to try the effect of removing part or all of the adrenal glands. But the early surgical attempts were failures: if too little adrenal tissue was removed, there was no effect on blood pressure; if too much was removed, patients died. Surgery became more successful when cortisone, an adrenal gland hormone, became available, allowing the adrenals to be removed completely and enough cortisone to be administered to maintain life.

Then in the 1950's there began to appear new drugs that could bring down elevated pressure through their effects on the nervous system. But they had to be used with caution. They were powerful agents—and if they caused too marked a reduction of pressure, there could be damage to vital organs. By restricting salt in the diet, doctors found that the drugs could be used in smaller, safer dosage. But not all patients responded to such measures.

Could a drug be found that would counteract the salt-retaining action of the adrenals? In 1958, one such drug, chlorothiazide, was found and was soon to be followed by several others highly effective in stimulating the kidneys to remove any excessive salt and water.

It was natural to try such agents, rather than restrict salt intake, as a means of increasing the effectiveness of the pressure-lowering compounds. And the trials were gratifying. Even the less potent pressure-lowering drugs became more effective when fortified by chlorothiazide or other similar agents, called diuretics.

Diuretics today rank among the most valuable drugs in medicine. Some act to block aldosterone, the adrenal hormone which is a powerful salt-retainer. Some promote salt excretion by depressing reabsorption by the kidney.

By promoting salt elimination, the diuretics of course also promote elimination of excess fluids, which follow the salt.

And elimination of excess fluids is important in many conditions besides hypertension.

In fact, fluid retention (called edema) will affect most of us at some point in our lives. It is no disease in itself but it occurs in connection with kidney, liver, heart and other diseases. Some 20 percent of pregnant women develop it apparently because of hormone changes. Regularly, almost every month, many women experience several days of premenstrual tension with edema and accompanying it such symptoms as irritability, depression and feelings of fullness in the abdomen.

Thanks to diuretics, edema can be overcome without need for extreme low-salt diets.

Such diets are distasteful; they require special foods and fussy preparation; and most patients find it difficult to stay on them.

The history of man's food habits shows there are no such things as good foods or bad. Individuals and whole nations have thrived on many different diets. And food customs indicate that there is nothing on earth which is not as much loved by one group of people as it is detested by another.

Except possibly salt.

Apropos of low-salt diets, one distinguished physician often liked to quote the passage in Alice Through the Looking Glass in which the King says, "There is nothing like eating hay when you're faint...I didn't say there was nothing better. I just said there is nothing like it."

Throughout his history, man has sought and loved salt. Perhaps, even beyond appreciating its ability to make good food taste better and even poor food somewhat more palatable, he recognized instinctively the body's need for it.

Salt can also be good medicine. Some of its medical uses go far back; some are relatively recent discoveries.

Solutions based upon salt have a long and honorable history in the emergency management of reduced blood volume caused by hemorrhage or shock. Because salt and water make up so much of the blood, a solution of 0.8 to 0.9 percent salt in water, called a physiological saline solution, is effective for temporarily restoring blood volume and saving life. It is readily available and generally safe.

In the emergency treatment of poisoning, when

the stomach must be washed out through a stomach tube, saline solution is often used.

Salt is commonly used now not only to treat heat prostration but to prevent it.

Veterinarians give salt orally to horses and cattle to treat indigestion, and apply salt solutions to irrigate deep wounds in animals. And dermatologists often apply salt solutions to inflamed skin lesions.

Thanks to the use of salt containing iodine there has been an almost miraculous change in people in regions which used to be referred to as the "goiter belts" — areas such as those in the Swiss Alps and around the North American Great Lakes. Only a few decades ago, visitors to such areas often were shocked by the number of people they saw, children as well as adults, disfigured by goiters — swellings of the thyroid gland, at the base of the throat, sometimes so large as to hamper breathing.

Without iodine, the thyroid gland cannot manufacture the normal quantity of its hormone, thyroxin. The hormone is 65 percent iodine. The thyroid, through its hormone output, is like a little machine that regulates the rate at which the body uses oxygen taken in by breathing — and also controls the rate at which various body organs function and the way the body utilizes food. Too little thyroid output can produce drowsiness, fatigue, apathy, weight gain, coarse features, thick and scaly skin.

When iodine intake is inadequate, the thyroid enlarges. It works excessively, even if not successfully, trying to produce enough hormone, swelling up in the process.

Now, merely through use of table salt to which a tiny amount of iodine has been added, simple goiter no longer characterizes the people who live in iodine-short areas that were once the goiter belts.

When man learned that chlorinating his water supplies would destroy the germs of many epidemic diseases, public health and the human lifespan gained the means to take tremendous strides, thanks again to the sciences and the salt that originated in the sea.

And as mankind increases its knowledge and understanding of its ancient marine heritage, oncoming civilizations will benefit from the resources of the sea.

— Lawrence Galton

Ancient Trails of Civilization

A philosophical French economist, Jean Bodin, wrote in 1568: "God distributed his favours in such a way that there is not a country in the world so fertile that it does not lack many things. God seems to have done this in order to keep all of the subjects of His Republic on a friendly basis."

Thus, man learned in early times that trade was necessary to his progress, his comfort, and often his life itself. Ideally, he traded his available materials for materials he needed upon a friendly basis. But whether it has been friendly or unfriendly, trade or exchange has always taken place.

The pathways that man has made in his search to discover and to use the gifts of the world have taken him around the earth and to the moon (1969).

The sum total of his pathways, his philosophies, his religions, his cultures, his arts and sciences, and his achievements can be called civilization. No one race, no one continent, no one culture can alone put a brand-mark upon civilization. All have contributed, traded, and developed parts of it in ways that are known and that are unknown.

A Japanese delegate, attending the International Congress of the History of Sciences at Jerusalem in 1953, expressed with graceful symbolism the essence of man's upward climb, in commenting on a discussion of China's contributions to science and civilization.

Speaking in French, S. Yajima of Tokyo said in part: *"Il y a plusiers routes pour escalader le Mont Fuji—le Fuji-yama. Mais toutes ses rejoignent au sommet. C'est la meme chose pour les civilizations."*

Facing page: *Civilizations grew where men found food, water, and salt—or could trade for them. The Middle East, a cradle of early cultures, was a source as well as a tradepoint for these essentials.*

"There are several routes to climb to the top of Mount Fuji—the Fuji-yama. But all join together at the summit. It is the same for civilizations."

There are many trails which can be traced upward towards the summit of civilization, as we see its summit in our time. Some trails are broken; some fade out; and others can only dimly be seen. Some stand out clearly.

Sooner or later, in following these trails back to their origins, the historian finds that each leads to a place on earth where, in addition to the sunshine and the air, man found available or could assemble for his use three essentials of life. These are salt, water, and food.

Sometimes early men (like modern men), in seeking their habitations, failed to realize that salt was as essential to life as food and water. Trade began when they became aware that they had to have salt to live. Salt was, historians say, probably one of the first articles of trade.

Ancient man knew the same salt sources that we know today—sea water; salty or brackish waters of springs, streams, wells, ponds, or lakes; salty earths and rock formations; salt deposits; underground salt mines; the salty ashes of land and marine vegetation; and—in a form used when salt was not otherwise available—in the meat and body fluids of animals.

For ages, man kept in motion, following the seasons and the food they brought. The earth, like man, did not stand still. Sometimes man's sources of food or drink vanished. Sometimes salt deposits played out or saline springs stopped flowing. Sometimes salt appeared at entirely new locations. Sometimes hunters or seamen found food, water, or salt resources far from their native settlements. Man advanced or retreated, lived or died, in the ways he responded to these changes.

The Greek, Herodotus, "Father of History," who wrote in the 5th Century B.C., described the North African settlements of Libya, in "a ridge of sand, reaching from Egyptian Thebes to the Pillars of Hercules [the Straits of Gibraltar]. Throughout this ridge, at the distance of about ten days' journey from one another,

heaps of salt in large lumps lie upon hills. At the top of every hill there gushes forth from the middle of the salt a stream of water, which is both cold and sweet. Around them dwell men who are the last inhabitants of Libya on the side of the desert." He went on to name and describe the tribes who lived at each of these locations. "Throughout the whole distance, at the end of every ten days' journey, there is a salt-mine, with people dwelling round it who all of them build their houses with blocks of the salt. No rain falls in these parts of Libya; if it were otherwise, the walls of these houses could not stand."

The great civilization centers of antiquity developed in river valleys where the three essentials of life existed: the Yellow River of China and the Indus River of India, in Eastern Asia; the Tigris, the Euphrates, and the Jordan Valleys of the Middle East; and the Nile Valley of Africa. Agriculture developed. Social structures formed. The large populations that grew in these centers expanded outward.

The ancient distribution pattern continued to be governed by the availability of salt, water, and food. Man took with him the knowledge and technology of the civilization from which he had come. In new locations, he and his descendants added to and enlarged this knowledge and technology. They found new challenges, new dangers, and new opportunities.

The Mediterranean Sea and its borderlands, generally rich in salt, water, and food, attracted many peoples. It became, more than any other region of the earth, the birthplace of civilizations and religions. The Jewish, Christian, and Mohammedan religions originated in the eastern borderlands of the Mediterranean, and spread over much of the world.

Three civilizations of particular significance to mankind developed in the Mediterranean. They were those of the Phoenicians, the Greeks, and the Romans.

The Phoenicians, the first maritime trading civilization, wove the Mediterranean world together with the connecting fabric of commerce.

They were a sea-faring people, the greatest of their times, and for centuries (1200-300 B.C.)

their ships carried most of the trade in the Mediterranean. They were land traders, too. Two caravan routes—one from the Euphrates Valley and another from Asia Minor—terminated in Phoenician port cities.

Phoenicia, a coastal strip about 200 miles long on the Mediterranean's eastern edge, was bounded on the north by ancient Syria, and on the south by ancient Palestine. It had available much water, fertile land, salt, and the sea.

The Phoenicians established a number of separate city-kingdoms which never formed a centralized nation, but which operated when necessary as a sort of confederacy to help in a common cause.

The first of the Phoenician cities was Sidon (the word means *fish*). The second was Tyre. Another was Byblus, an exporter of papyrus, whose name survives in connection with books and the Bible. Acre, important in the Christian Crusades many centuries later, was another. The cedars of Lebanon were shipped from Phoenicia to be used in King Solomon's temple in Jerusalem.

The Phoenicians' early trade was with Egypt and Assyria, where they traded timber and their other goods for products that they were soon carrying along the coast north of Phoenicia to settlements in Asia Minor, Greece, and Italy.

Among the products they traded were salt, salt-fish, grains, hides, papyrus, glassware and pottery, textiles, rare woods, fine metal work, cosmetics, spices, scents, and other luxury goods.

Tyre produced a purple dye from shellfish and salt that was often imitated but not equalled. It was coveted, expensive, and became the royal purple of princes and emperors. The standard of quality of Phoenician workmanship, manufactures, and goods was the highest of its time.

The Phoenicians were not a creative people in the arts and sciences. Nor were they a philosophical or a literary people. They did have a remarkable talent for improving what they inherited or learned from other civilizations. This talent, which was oriented toward commerce and colonization, ranged from ship design to the development of an alphabet. They needed a system of writing to keep records of their trade and credit arrangements. The Phoenician alphabet became a keystone of western civilization.

Through trade and colonization, the Phoenicians gave to the Greeks, to the people who became the Romans, and to the entire Mediterranean basin the alphabet, alphabetic writing, arithmetic, and weights and measures. They did not invent any of these; they improved them from less useful earlier forms, and transmitted them to later civilizations.

Great names float in and out of the records of Phoenicia — Canaan, Chaldea, Egypt, Syria, Babylonia, Palestine, Judea, Assyria, Lebanon, Arabia, India, Persia, Scythia, Crete, Macedonia, Athens, Sparta, Byzantium, Greece, Rome, and Carthaginia.

Phoenicians put early colonies on a number of islands, all of which had ample salt as well as other products valuable for trade. Cyprus had copper, gold, silver, grains, wines, and olive oil; Rhodes had harbors, forests, grains, fruits, and olives; Crete, center of an earlier civilization, had developed pottery, metal work, and sculpture. When the Greeks contested them for these islands, the Phoenicians withdrew and went westward with their colonies.

The Phoenician cities began establishing North African colonies in the 12th Century B.C., when they founded Utica, on the Bay of Tunis. It had a good river, a good salt supply, a good harbor site for development, a fertile land area, and metals in the hills behind the coast.

Carthage, founded by Tyre about 822 B.C. in what is now Tunisia, was a later colony. It became a great power, established colonies of its own, and later challenged Rome for the supremacy of the Mediterranean and the western world. Several other Phoenician settlements were placed on the middle coast of North Africa about the same time.

The Phoenicians also put colonies on Sicily, Pantellaria, Lampedusa, Malta, Sardinia, the Balearic Islands, and the Spanish peninsula.

Metals, salt, water, fish, other food sources, and the development of profitable trade with native populations led them onward.

In Spain, they established Gadir (*stronghold*), now Cadiz, a great harbor west of the Straits of Gibraltar, in a region rich in fisheries and salt; Malacca (*salt,* in Phoenician), now Malaga; Tartessus, also known as Tarshish, noted in Athens for its salted eels and tunny fish, and several others.

Spain had many other valuable assets — gold, silver, lead, copper, iron, tin, wool, wines, grain, and salt pork.

Phoenicians also went to the Scilly Isles and to Cornwall, in Britain, to get tin, lead, and hides, for which they traded to the natives salt, earthenware, and bronze vessels.

Over the centuries, Phoenicia's position — which was never easily attained or maintained — declined and vanished under the onslaughts of changing power balances. Alexander the Great crushed Phoenicia in 332 B.C. Its heritage passed on to newer civilizations.

The first of these to rise was Greece, which was also the first great civilization in continental Europe. Greece owed much to Crete, the island which had also been important to Phoenicia, but also much to the peoples who migrated from northern lands about 2000 B.C. The rest of the world was to owe much to Greece.

In a small land, rugged and rocky, deeply indented with bays and gulfs of the sea, the Greeks developed a culture and a civilization which have radiated throughout the world.

No part of Greece was more than 30 miles from sea water. Greece's terrain, difficult to travel by land and difficult to make produce sufficient food, pointed her inhabitants towards the sea, sea trade, and colonization. Geographical limitations also directed the growth of urban life into hundreds of small city-states, which formed where the necessities of life could be obtained for limited numbers of people.

The land was short in resources and long on people. Greek colonies went to the numerous islands that fringed the coasts; to the Mediter-ranean shores of Asia, and to the Black Sea; to the African coast, to Sicily, to the Italian peninsula, to Massilia (Marseilles), and to Spain. These colonies supplied Greece with salted and pickled fish, grain, oil, metals, timber, and other native products. The Greeks were excellent traders, colonizers, and fighters. They were good seamen, but not bold navigators or explorers. They preferred to stay in sight of land and to travel only during daylight hours.

Greece improved upon the Phoenician alphabet, and in using it produced an intellectual and cultural explosion such as the world had never before seen. It continued through and beyond the many bitter wars the city-states fought amongst themselves, through the Greek wars with Persia, the campaigns of Alexander the Great, and for hundreds of years thereafter.

The Greek philosophers laid the foundations of investigative and speculative thought in sciences, arts, politics, social institutions, ethics, moralities, and metaphysics.

Among them were Socrates, Plato, Aristotle, Epicurus, and Zeno. Their influence continues in the world of today.

The Greek mathematical scientists included Archimedes, who discovered the principle of specific gravity; Euclid, who developed a system of geometry; and Pythagoras, whose name will also be forever associated with geometry.

In astronomy, the Greeks included Eratosthenes, who in the 3rd Century B.C. calculated the circumference of the earth within an accuracy of 50 miles; Hipparchus, who made the first attempt to map and catalogue the stars; Claudius Ptolemy, whose maps proved to be influential in the discovery of the New World; and Aristarchus of Samos, who in the 3rd Century B.C. demonstrated that the earth and other planets revolved around the sun. Aristarchus was not believed.

The Greek physician Hippocrates, the Father of Medicine, and a later Greek physician, Galen, wrote works that were fundamental influences in the medical arts.

The Father of History, Herodotus, and the first scientific historian, Thucydides, wrote books that are still studied.

In literature and the arts, Homer's epic poems on the Greek war with Troy and the wanderings of Ulysses; the dramas of Aeschylus, Sophocles, and Aristophanes; the fables of Aesop; the sculpture of Phidias and Praxiteles; and Grecian architecture are only a few of the inspired works of the civilization that rose suddenly like the sun in this Eastern Mediterranean land.

The best geography of ancient times was written by a Greek, Strabo, born in 63 B.C., long after Greece had ceased to be the leading political power of the Mediterranean world. The decline of Greece as a political power did not result in its decline as a cultural power. In his geography, Strabo describes many places of the Greek and Roman world, and includes comments indicating the importance of salt and the fisheries of his time.

In Spain, he mentions Menlaria, Belon, New Carthage (Cartagena) and Turdetania as fish-salting centers; and Lusitania and Turdetania as sites of salt quarries. He also mentions saltworks in many other areas, such as the Crimea, where the salt was produced at works on a lagoon. There were scores of them.

He mentioned trouble which arose over salt between two peoples in the Balkans:

"Now the Autariatae were once the largest and best tribe of the Illyrians. In earlier times they were continually at war with the Ardiaei over the saltworks on the common frontiers. The salt was made to crystallize out of water which in the springtime flowed at the foot of a certain mountain glen; for if they drew off the water and stowed it away for five days the salt would become thoroughly crystallized. They would agree to use the saltworks alternately, but would break the agreements and go to war."

On the shores of the western Mediterranean, and on its islands, the Greeks began running into the activities of two rising imperial powers. Greece itself, for all its brilliance as a center of culture, had never become a well-organized nation. Its city-states, sometimes with the assistance of other powers such as Persia and Rome, had constantly fought each other for supremacy. Greece never developed an effective administrative or legal system to unify it as a nation. Greece is said by some to have "committed suicide" by this lack of unity among its states. Rome eventually took over Greece and the Grecian colonies.

The two rising western powers were Carthage, in North Africa, and Rome, in Italy.

Carthage had stepped into the position of leadership of the Phoenician colonies after Alexander the Great destroyed Tyre in 332 B.C. Carthage had taken over Sicily, Sardinia, Corsica, Malta, the Balearic Islands, and some other islands in the Mediterranean. It had taken over Cadiz and had established other colonies in Spain, including New Carthage (Cartagena). It had explored for gold and slaves down the coast of west Africa. It became wealthy, and was the greatest naval power in the Mediterranean. It threatened both Greece and the rising Republic of Rome.

In a series of three wars (the Punic Wars), fought between 264 and 146 B.C., Rome defeated and destroyed Carthage, and took over its possessions and its people. Over the ruins of the city of Carthage, the Romans sowed salt as a symbol of destruction.

The Romans were the first successful imperial people of antiquity. Though they did not excel in trade and seamanship, as the Phoenicians and the Carthaginians did, or in science, art, literature, and philosophy as the Greeks did, they developed improved systems of government, civil administration, military organization, roads, public utilities, and law.

Their talents in these fields enabled them to develop a more widespread empire than had been accomplished by any previous Mediterranean civilization.

The Roman Empire, which was first a kingdom and later a republic before it became an empire, originated in a city that grew on a formation of hills about 15 miles from the mouth of the Tiber River, near the western coastal midsection of the Italian peninsula. The region, called Latium, was agricultural, and had a number of settlements. Rome, founded in 753 B.C., was one of them.

Rome's location was well chosen. It controlled the ford across the river on the ancient trail by which the Sabine people from the mountains northeast of Rome went to the sea marshes at the mouth of the Tiber for salt, a trail which was later improved and became the Via Salaria (the Salt Way). The marshes at the Tiber's mouth were claimed by an Etruscan tribe, a people north of the Tiber, of a more advanced civilization than the Latiums.

Rome exacted tolls for the use of the ford and the path through its territory. One of Rome's earliest wars, fought against the Etruscans, had as its objective the control of the salt-works at the mouth of the Tiber. Rome gained them in the 6th Century B.C., and established Ostia, its first colony, there. The Via Salaria was the first of Rome's roads of empire.

Eventually, 19 arterial roads, connecting imperial provinces throughout the empire, led to Rome.

Rome reached its greatest territorial extent in 117 A.D., under the rule of Trajan, its first Spanish emperor. The empire extended in Europe from Britain in the west to the Rhine, the Danube, and beyond into Dacia (Rumania), and eastward to the Black Sea. In Africa it included Mauretania (Morocco) and the coastal lands east through Egypt. In Asia it included all of Armenia, the Tigris-Euphrates Valley, Syria, Palestine, and part of Arabia as well as all the lands west of these territories. Rome's territorial decline began under the next emperor, Hadrian (another Spaniard), who withdrew from Armenia, Mesopotamia, and Assyria.

At the peak, the Roman Empire had 100,000,000 citizens and used 1,000,000 tons of salt a year. The Empire's best-known salt sources were located in or near Ostia, Volaterra, and Taranto, in Italy; Utica and some Libyan sites in North Africa; Gela and Agrigenta in Sicily; Cartagena, in Spain; the Mediterranean and Atlantic coasts of France; Epirus, Illyria, and Thessaly, in the Balkans; Egypt; Asia Minor; Cyprus; and ancient Palestine.

The Romans thoroughly investigated the resources of the lands they took in their conquests. The saltworks and sources, mines, and quarries became the possessions of the emperors.

Ships from many ports supplied Rome and its provinces. The Romans called the Mediterranean "Mare Nostrum" (Our Sea).

But Rome never became a great trading nation. As the historian Tenney Frank pointed out, "The importance of trade was seldom clearly understood during the Empire. The directors of the state had no need or desire to attempt a balancing of trade between Rome and the provinces: they did not seem interested in who carried the goods; they did not concern themselves greatly when Gaul and Spain captured the markets that formerly belonged to the producers of Italy; and the expensive importations from the East were to them not so much a question of danger to Italian production as of the depletion of precious metals that flowed beyond reach. The emperors did not depart from the ancient custom of laissez-faire: 'mercantilism' and 'protection' were never seriously tried."

A list of Rome's exports and imports demonstrates this clearly: the Italian peninsula's trade was chiefly with Rome, and included wines, olive oil, ironware and bronzeware, pottery, ointments, pitch, lumber, grain, pork, wool, and cloth.

Imports to Italy and Rome from Asia, Syria, Egypt, Marseilles, and Spain included grain, salt, timber, dried fruit, precious stones, wines, tapestries, draperies, rugs, glassware, dyes, cloth, linens, cedars of Lebanon, silk, cotton, pearls, ivory, spices, incense, myrrh, paper, ivory, animals for the Roman games, black slaves, metals, hides, wool, salt meat, cheese, amber, tin, metal products, olive oil, wheat, fish, leather, and salt pork.

The Romans did understand taxation. Augustus Caesar, who never assumed the imperial title but was regarded as the first and one of the greatest of the Roman emperors, reigned for 43 years, from 27 B.C. The Christian Bible tells us, "And it came to pass in those days, that there went out a decree from Caesar Augustus, that all the world should be taxed." Joseph and Mary were in Bethlehem when Jesus Christ was born because they had gone there to be counted in the census on which the Roman taxes were based.

Extensive lists of salt sources taxed by Rome exist.

In the 1st Century A.D., the Emperors Vespasian and his son Titus seized the deserts around the Dead Sea, and Jerusalem. Salt had been produced there from prehistoric times. The objective of the campaign was to secure the salt, according to a study made in 1963 by M. R. Bloch of the Technical Advisory Board of the Government of Israel, because the level of the world's seas was rising and the coastal salt works of most of the world were being destroyed.

By 500 A.D., the sea levels had risen six feet, Bloch's study showed, and he concluded that the salt from the Dead Sea, the desert lakes, and mines kept European civilizations from collapsing until the sea level fell sufficiently for Europe to recommence producing salt from sea water by the 10th Century A.D.

Rome gave western civilization a common language, a stable economic and political system, advanced technology, and a great stimulus to commerce. The Romans used 13 passes through the Alps. The Roman roads, built for military and administrative purposes, became channels of trade.

The sites of many of the Roman garrisons and colonies grew into notable cities. A few of them are: Constantinople, Carthage (rebuilt by Julius Caesar), London, Zurich, Basel, Geneva, Cologne, Mainz, Windisch, Augsburg, Salzburg, Vienna, Tarragona, Merida, Arles, Lyons, Narbonne, Bologna, Genoa, Milan, Turin, and Venice.

Under the Romans, western Europe enjoyed an early and significant industrial development. The Romans encouraged and profited by the increased industry and manufacturing of their provinces. They provided a foundation for great trade.

Rome's agricultural and imperial basis served it well for many centuries. Under strong leaders, its system worked effectively. As its leadership deteriorated, its imperial structure fell apart. When the Roman Empire of the West fell, in 476 A.D., Western Europe suffered through the centuries known as the Dark Ages for the lack of a strong trading system, as well as for the lack of a strong imperial system.

—William W. Boddie

The Middle Ages:
A Potent Influence

By the end of the 11th Century, Europe was entering the last stages of the Middle Ages, and it was a good thing for civilization that it was.

The worst phases of feudalism, the power structure which developed in Western Europe following the destruction of the Roman Empire of the West, were beginning to disappear — though remnants survived to plague the world for some centuries.

The feudal system had become dominant because there were no leaders powerful and prosperous enough to organize, control, and perpetuate a widespread empire. A few capable emperors, working with the Roman Catholic Popes, were able to pull together for temporary periods large realms under the name of the Holy Roman Empire.

But not even Charlemagne, the greatest of these emperors, was able to exert his imperial power over all of his empire. For example, the city of Venice refused to submit to Charlemagne, and there was nothing that he could do about it.

He, like his successors who wore the crown of the Holy Roman Empire for many centuries, simply lacked the power, the money, the armies, the legal organization, and the practiced administrative structure of the earlier Roman Emperors.

Under the feudal system, numerous kings (under whatever titles they used) seized and held power over such territories as they could. They usually swore allegiance to the Holy Roman Emperor, or some other overlord, and pledged him certain agreed-upon military, financial, and other types of support. The kings, in turn, delegated control over parts of their kingdoms to a power structure of subordinate nobility, each member of which pledged loyalty and support to his own superior, or liege lord.

Facing page: *Venice, by its seaborne commerce with Constantinople in the Middle Ages, was the door through which Western Europe received both trade goods and knowledge vital to the revival of a stagnating civilization.*

This seemed to the kings and emperors to be a workable method of controlling their domains. But in practice, the feudal system resulted in the development of many rival and belligerent leaders, who established many independent realms of their own. Each of these sought to become self-sufficient, to supply all its own needs—for food, clothing, weapons, men—and the chief objective of many of them was to take over, by military force, strategic marriages, assassinations, or other methods, the territory and possessions of similar neighboring rulers.

By and large, the feudal ages were marked by continual military and political power struggles. In many of the struggles, fathers fought against sons; brothers murdered or poisoned each other; the hangman's rope and the headsman's axe were put in frequent use.

The economic basis of feudalism was agriculture, land, and the people and resources that the lords controlled. The times were, to put it mildly, unsettled and dangerous for lords and peasants alike.

Insofar as possible, trade between the estates was eliminated. No estate sought to produce more than it needed for its own residents—there was no organized marketing system to dispose of surplus products.

But in three commodities, trade did not cease. They were salt, iron, and textiles. Not all estates could supply their own. Those located where these commodities existed and were produced continued to sell them to others.

On the roads and waterways to and from these product sources, the feudal lords who had the power to do so laid levies or tolls upon the traders whose routes crossed their estates, and increased their own scanty revenues.

Thus the framework of roads, shipping, and communication was kept open in Europe for the later revival of trade, the growth of cities and towns, and the establishment of industry and commerce.

When these began developing as the Middle Ages moved on, the eventual doom of feudalism was being sealed. The towns which were involved became "non-feudal islands in feudal seas."

Some feudal lords encouraged the expansion of trade and cities in their territories. They recognized them as sources of wealth. The rulers of Flanders and The Netherlands were among them. Thus, an influential part of the economic development of the Middle Ages took place in this region.

Ships bringing cargoes from the north, where the Hanseatic League was formed, or from the south, from which the ships and galleys of Venice and Genoa brought articles of commerce, or from England or Spain, could be sure of return cargoes, including iron, salt, textiles, and many other goods. It was a midway meeting ground for Europe's international trade.

The city of Bruges, in modern Belgium, was the emporium where the sea-borne trade of the Mediterranean, the Baltic, the Atlantic coast of Europe, and the British Isles met. Later in the Middle Ages, the emporium became Antwerp.

However, this development came slowly and followed in the wake of more spectacular events. One involved England, another the Mediterranean.

Duke William of Normandy seized England in 1066 with the assistance of his feudal Norman barons. There, as William the Conqueror, he initiated the beginnings of a governmental structure that evolved over the next few centuries into an English national state which is still presided over by his descendants.

The author of *The Anglo-Saxon Chronicle,* in recording the actions of the Normans, wrote a realistic account of the method King William used to tighten his control over England and his own Norman feudal subordinates, and at the same time to find out the property and resources he owned and could use and tax to defend and extend his possessions.

"...The King had a great council [in 1085] and very deep speech with his 'witan' [council] about this land, how it was peopled, or by what men; then he sent his men over all England, into every shire, and caused to be ascertained how many hundred hides were in the shire, or what dues he sought to have in 12 months from the shire," according to the Chronicler. [A *hide* in Anglo-Saxon England was the amount of land that could be plowed in one day by a single team of eight oxen.]

"Also he caused to be written how much land his archbishops had and his suffragan bishops and his abbots and his earls; and—though I may narrate somewhat prolixly—what or how much each man had who was a landholder in England, in land, or in cattle, and how much money it might be worth. So very narrowly he caused it to be traced out, that there was not one single hide, nor even one yard of land, nor even—it is shame to tell, though it seemed to him no shame to do—an ox, nor a cow, nor a swine, left that was not set down in his writ."

This written inventory was brought to William personally. The saltworks on the English coasts were among the resources which William had listed in *The Domesday Book*, as it was later called. There were 1,195 saltworks.

[William's mother was the daughter of Fulbert of Falaise, in Normandy. Fulbert was a tanner—who used salt in the medieval process of making leather from animal skins.]

The Chronicler evaluated William as "a very wise man, and very powerful, more dignified and strong than any of his predecessors were. He was mild to the good men who loved God, and beyond all measure severe to the men who gainsaid his will . . . So also was he a very rigid and cruel man, so that no one durst do anything against his will.

But, continued the writer, "among other good things is not to be forgotten the good peace that he made in this land; so that a man who had any confidence in himself might go over his realm, with his bosom full of gold, unhurt."

Southeast of the Mediterranean, in Arabia, the Prophet Mohammed (c. 569-632 A.D.) established the religion he called Islam. It had far-reaching effects upon Western Europe.

Within 50 years of the Prophet's death, Islam had swept like a whirlwind east and west from Arabia to the shores of the China Sea and the Atlantic Ocean.

The Mohammedans had unsuccessfully attacked Constantinople, capital of the Byzantine Empire (the Roman Empire of the East) in 713. Thereafter, they had seized other parts of the Byzantine Empire, including Jerusalem, the Holy Land of the Christian religion.

The Mohammedans—or Moors, or Saracens, as they were variously called—moved from North Africa across the Straits of Gibraltar in 711, seized the Iberian Peninsula, and soon crossed the Pyrenees into France. Charles Martel, the grandfather of Charlemagne, turned them back from France into Spain in 732.

The Mediterranean, which the Romans had called "Mare Nostrum" (Our Sea), became a Moslem lake. The Saracens took command of the western part of the sea, seizing Sicily, Sardinia, Corsica, and the Balearic Islands.

They harried the Mediterranean coasts of France and Italy, and closed off the trade in spices, luxury fabrics, and other goods, which Syrian ships had been developing with Europe, principally through the port of Marseilles.

The threat of Islam to Western Christendom, and the seizure of Jerusalem, were seeds planted in Europe which slowly grew into the Christian Crusades.

Of more immediate significance, but a significance which influenced Western civilization for many centuries, was the opportunity which the closing of the western Mediterranean trade by the Saracens gave to the city of Venice to become the intermediary between Constantinople and Western Europe.

Venice was located upon a number of sandy, barren, offshore islands near the head of the Adriatic Sea. These islands, separated by lagoons from each other and from the North Italian mainland, had originally been settled (before the 5th Century) by a race of people who managed to survive there, where they had no apparent resources, not even drinking water. They made salt in the lagoons, caught fish and salted them, and traded the salt and salt fish with mainland dwellers for food, drink, wood to build fishing boats, and other materials.

From time to time, as in 452, when Attila the Hun sacked northern Italy, mainlanders fled to these easily-defended islands as a refuge. But the refugees generally returned to the mainland as soon as the pressure from the barbarian invaders lessened. It was not until the Lombard invasion of 568 that most of them finally abandoned the mainland for Venice.

There they found safety. They also found opportunity. They continued the earlier trade in salt and salt fish for food, drink, and wood. They built ships with the wood. These new Venetians took advantage of Venice's favorable location for trade with the East.

They commenced carrying salt, salt fish, slaves, and wood to Constantinople, and bringing back luxury products. From Venice, these goods went overland through the mountain passes or by inland waters to customers in Northern Italy and other parts of Europe.

Venice's trade with Constantinople and the Eastern Mediterranean gave her not only great wealth but also knowledge that fostered a remarkable industrial and commercial development in Northern Italy, and that greatly influenced the revival of trade.

Textiles, glass, fine leather-work, metals, banking, insurance, credit, and other necessities of international trade were among the contributions Northern Italy made to Western Europe.

The Moslem blockade of the Mediterranean ended during the First Crusade (1097). Trade by sea recommenced with Western Europe.

Another very important center of trade was situated north of Flanders and The Netherlands, where earlier associations of German towns later became the Hanseatic League.

The Hanseatic League was a confederation of trading towns, most of them located on good harbors or deep rivers in the area of Northern Germany. The League's membership ranged from as few as 52 towns to as many as 70 or 80. The confederation gave the towns economic and military power which the Kings of Germany (or the Holy Roman Emperors) were unable to provide them in feudal times.

When the King of Denmark went to war with Sweden and interfered with the League's profitable participation in the Baltic fishing industry, the League joined forces with the King of Sweden, took Copenhagen, and dictated terms of the Treaty of Stralsund (1370) that gave the League free passage through the Sound, free trade in Denmark's territory, and charge of the herring market. The Sound was the Baltic's waterway to the North Sea.

New German colonies were established under sponsorship of the Hanseatic League upon the Baltic's largely-unpopulated shores to capitalize upon the resources available there, and to consume the products that the League's cities traded for or made.

The products that the new settlements brought into the Hanseatic league trade included luxury furs, fish, grain, beer, honey, wax, timber, and potash (a chemical produced from wood ashes).

The products that the Hanseatic merchants purchased from other areas included the textile and metal products produced in Flanders, and salt, iron, wine, wool, and tin, as well as the luxury products produced in Northern Italy, the East, the Mediterranean, and the Byzantine Empire.

In the later Middle Ages, when the numbers of towns increased and their populations grew, the core of international trade involved foodstuffs and, necessarily, the salt required to preserve them. Local markets, supplied from the production of the countryside, were not adequate to feed the larger concentrations of city dwellers, who produced goods to trade, but not enough food to eat. It was necessary to bring food longer distances, often by water.

Famine in parts of Europe was an ever-present threat (as it still is in many parts of the world). The agricultural system often failed to produce sufficient foodstuffs for people, and generally did not produce sufficient forage for animals to live during the winter months. Europeans who owned livestock animals slaughtered their winter's supply of meat in the autumn, when the weather was cold, and heavily salted it to preserve it. Breeding stock was kept alive and fed, awaiting the new crops of the next spring.

Butter and cheese, much eaten instead of meat, were preserved by the use of one-tenth their weight in salt.

England, which was comparatively more fortunate in food production than many other areas of Europe, experienced a famine on an average of once every 14 years during the 11th and 12th Centuries. These famines lasted a total of 20 years, or ten percent of the two centuries.

It was to the sea and its marine life that Medieval Europe looked largely for its food. The fishing boats of coastal kingdoms and domains brought ashore cargoes of herring, cod, shellfish, salmon, haddock, sturgeon, mackerel, and many other types of fish. Ashore, the rivers and lakes were farmed for freshwater fish to eat, with traps, weirs, and nets.

The Roman Catholic meatless days, and the Christian season of Lent, encouraged the eating of fish. In the Earl of Northumberland's household in England, stockfish, salt fish, white herring, red herring, salt salmon, and salt eels were common provisions for every meal. For breakfast, the Earl and Countess were served two pieces of salt fish, six baconed herring, three white herring, or a dish of sprats. Breakfast during Lent for Lord Percy, the son and heir, age 11, was three salted herring or some sprats, some salt fish, bread, butter, and beer.

Above all else, the herring was Europe's most dependable source of food. There were enormous herring fisheries in the Baltic, the North Sea, the English Channel, and the waters around Iceland and Ireland. Workers by the thousands were engaged in catching, preserving, and selling the herring, as well as in eating it.

One of the two major centers of the herring

industry was located in the Western Baltic at the Swedish towns of Falsterbö and Skanör on the Sound—the 70-mile long strait between Denmark and Sweden that had been forced open in 1370 by Sweden and the Hanseatic League.

The other center, off the east coast of England, was fished jointly by the English and the Dutch [the Netherlanders]. The English industry was centered around Yarmouth and Scarborough; the Dutch, around Brielle. It was no coincidence that these centers of the herring industry were located where salt was available in great quantities to cure the fish.

In order to be of good quality, the cured herring had to be salted within 24 hours after being taken from the sea. If it were to be cured as white herring, it was then packed in more salt in kegs. If it were to be cured as red herring, it was smoked and salted.

The salt most highly-prized by those engaged in the Baltic fishing industry was produced from brine springs at Lüneburg, and marketed through Lübeck. Lübeck, which had dug a canal to the Elbe River so that the salt could be transported across the Jutland Peninsula, was then the leading city of the Hanseatic League, and was the League's port on the Baltic. Lüneburg was of course a Hanseatic town. Among other influential Hanseatic towns were Hamburg, Bremen, Cologne, Dortmund, Groningen, Hanover, and Magdeburg.

A detailed description of brine boiling and several other methods of salt production in the Middle Ages was written by Georgius Agricola, a German physician and an authority on minerals and mining. He spent 20 years preparing his greatest work, *De Re Metallica, (On Minerals)*, which was published in Latin in 1556. It was translated into English in 1912 by Mr. and Mrs. Herbert C. Hoover [Mr. Hoover served as President of the United States in 1928-32.].

According to Agricola, the brine was drawn from the wells and poured into 12-gallon casks. Porters carried the casks into the boiling sheds. If the brine were very strong, it was poured by the dipperful into the boiling caldrons directly. If the brine were weak, it was put in a small tub and mixed with salt to increase its salinity before being run into the boiling caldron.

The walls of the boiling sheds were made from baked earth, or from mud-covered wickerwork, or from stones or bricks. The exterior walls and interior partitions were high—16 to 40 feet—and the wooden roofs were thickly plastered underneath and on top with a mixture of straw and mud or clay cement to prevent fires and to retain heat.

The fireplaces, made of clay and salt moistened with brine, were 8½ feet long, 7¾ feet wide, 6 feet high if the fuel to be used in the boiling was straw, or nearly 4 feet high if wood was the fuel. Fire hardened the construction materials.

The boiling caldrons were made of riveted sheets of iron or lead, in rectangular form, and smeared over with a cement of oxblood, oxliver, and ashes, to prevent leaks. They were 8 feet long, 7 feet wide, and 6 inches high. The caldrons were supported on the walls of the furnaces by a structure of iron beams and hooks. An opening of 8 inches was left at the rear of the furnace to allow the escape of smoke and flames. A wooden hood led the smoke to windows in the back wall and the ceiling.

"From thirty-seven dippersful of brine the master or his deputy, at Halle in Saxony, makes two cone-shaped pieces of salt," wrote Agricola. [A dipperful was 1¼ gallons.] "Each master has a helper, or in place of a helper his wife assists him in his work, and, in addition, a youth who throws wood or straw under the caldron. He, on account of the great heat of the workshop, wears a straw cap on his head and a breech cloth, being otherwise quite naked. As soon as the master has poured the first dipperful of brine into the caldron, the youth sets fire to the wood and straw laid under it. If the firewood is bundles of faggots or brushwood, the salt will be white, but if straw is burned, then it is not infrequently blackish, for the sparks, which are drawn up with the smoke into the hood, fall down again into the water and color it black.

"In order to accelerate the condensation of the brine, when the master has poured in two casks and as many dippersful of brine, he adds about a Roman *cyathus* [1⅕ pints] of bullock's blood, or of calf's blood, or buck's blood, or else he mixes it into the nineteenth dipperful of brine, in order that it may be dissolved and distributed into all the corners of the caldron; in other places, the blood is dissolved in beer. When the boiling water seems to be mixed with scum, he skims it with a ladle; this scum, if he be working with rock-salt, he throws into the opening in the furnace through which the smoke escapes, and it is dried into rock-salt; if it be not from rock-salt, he pours it on to the floor of the workshop. From the beginning to the boiling and skimming is the work of half-

Lübeck, through which Lunebürg salt was shipped. Before, western goods destined for the Baltic markets had been shipped to Hamburg. There they had been unloaded and carried by land across the Jutland Peninsula to Lübeck, which shipped them on.

After the sea route through the Sound was opened, the Dutch Hanseatic towns began shipping Bay salt into the Baltic by the water route, avoiding the costs of transhipping altogether.

The Bay salt was welcomed in the Baltic, despite its poorer quality. It was a third to a half cheaper than Lüneburg salt.

Other Hanseatic towns and Dutch towns also began shipping Bay salt to the Baltic by the same route. The conflict of interests, eventually brought to a head by the salt trade, led to the disintegration of the Hanseatic League, although there were other conflicts involved, too.

Lüneburg salt's high quality was still acknowledged. There were other German brine sources in the Baltic region and more German salt sources south of Lüneburg at Sülldorf, Stassfurt, and Halle. Lüneburg and Lübeck used their connections with German and other royal powers to block this salt from entering the Baltic. These efforts were not so effective as they were expensive. Lüneburg continued to supply the Scania fisheries. It was not able to expand elsewhere.

Yet throughout Europe, the demands for salt were increasing. In the Mediterranean, there was a brisk trade in solar salt and in salt from mines and other deposits.

The trade of the ancient salt mines in the Eastern Alps—Hallstadt and Hallein—was reviving. In the Erzebirge (Ore Mountains), the most thriving metal-producing area of Central Europe, numerous "fluxes" which contained salt were being used in the producing and refining of metal.

Bay salt became the major supplier of Europe in this time of need, and despite wars and devastations, the trade continued during the Middle Ages.

Bay salt first entered Europe's international trade after the English King Henry II married Eleanor of Aquitaine in 1152 and acquired her vast possessions in the present area of Southwest France.

English ships, and others, going to the ports of Bordeaux or La Rochelle for cargoes of wine, loaded solar salt available at the same ports.

Wines and other products made in the areas of large salt sources entered international trade in this manner. Bay salt helped accelerate the trend, unwittingly started by the Romans, of shifting the center of Western civilization from the Mediterranean to the shores of the Atlantic.

It helped destroy feudalism and develop the concepts of national identity in France and England.

Of all the taxes which the kings of France put upon their subjects, the gabelle (salt tax) was the most harsh and the most hated. "In Brittany," wrote the historian Thomas Carlyle in The French Revolution, "they once rose in revolt at the first introduction of Pendulum Clocks, thinking it had something to do with the gabelle." The abuse of the gabelle by the French kings, who exempted the nobility and privileged classes from the tax and thus threw the entire burden of paying the tax upon the peasants, merchants, craftsmen, and other non-privileged classes, was one of the causes of the French Revolution. This revolution ended the feudal "Old Regime" of France.

Feudal battles between kings of England and the French kings had taken place since the time of William the Conqueror, who was Duke of Normandy, as well as King of England. The French kings were the feudal overlords of domains belonging to the English kings. The English kings had to fight to keep these possessions out of the hands of the French.

The marriage of Henry II of England to Eleanor of Aquitaine vastly increased the holdings in France of the English crown. Nearly 200 years after Henry II, the English King Edward III in 1337 invaded France. Edward not only refused to admit that King Philip VI of France was his overlord, he claimed that he himself was the rightful King of France. Thus he began the Hundred Years War between France and England. It was the last of the great feudal wars.

The war ended in defeat for the English in 1453, when Edward's great-great-grandson, Henry VI, was king.

During this war, Joan of Arc appeared as the savior of France when the English were besieging Orleans in 1429. The French were then at the edge of final defeat. But Joan inspired the French people with a spirit of nationalism that had never before existed there. It was 24 years later before the last English army left Bordeaux, and the war was over. Joan was burned at the stake as a heretic in Rouen in 1431.

Much of the war, which was one of extraordinary devastation, was fought in the Aquitaine regions. The flourishing wine and salt trade was destroyed.

But in the Brittany area of Bourgneuf Bay, the salt trade continued. Some salt trade also went to Spain and Portugal.

Bourgneuf Bay was about 20 miles wide. Geographically, it lay in the territories of several feudal powers. Its rights, privileges, and allegiances were quite complex, even for feudal times. But its salt was important to all of Europe, and although it did not entirely escape the ravages of the Hundred Years War, no feudal power cared to upset the delicate balance that existed there and stop the production of the salt.

On two occasions when French kings threatened to impose the *gabelle* upon parts of the Bay—in 1383 and 1451—they dropped their plans when the salt producers and the salt traders insisted they would be put out of business.

The Duke of Brittany, the overlord of the northern part of the Bay, eliminated his taxes on grain which had to be imported to feed the saltmakers of Guerande. Sufficient food could not be grown locally. He—and other feudal lords of the salt-producing areas—encouraged and gave special privileges to traders who came for the salt.

The Hanseatic cities in the 1370's made a safe-conduct treaty with the Duke of Brittany. They began sending a "Bay Fleet," which assembled near Bruges, and went south for the salt and returned in convoy.

In returning from the Bay, some of the ships turned off to supply the English market at London; others went to Bruges, where a daily salt market was held; and still others continued on into the Baltic. The salt was distributed from Bruges through a wide area.

The Dutch shippers competed successfully with the Hanseatic merchants for the European carrying trade, in addition to the salt trade.

The Dutch success contributed greatly to the decline and finally the end of the Hanseatic League. The Netherlands had begun to become a major center for world trade, shipping, and later for colonization of other parts of the world.

In a curious sort of parallel, The Netherlands rose, as Venice had in earlier centuries, to world leadership upon the foundation of fish and salt.

—*William W. Boddie*

The Silent Trade of Timbuktu

"**M**ankind can live without gold but not without salt."

If the Roman official and historian Cassiodorus (490-583 A.D.) was looking towards Africa when he made that profound observation, he was looking in a singularly appropriate direction.

There was a striking reversal in the values which certain parts of Africa and certain parts of Europe placed upon salt and gold.

Rome—in fact, Europe—had never produced large quantities of gold. Gold's great value was proportionate to its scarcity, the great difficulties in securing and protecting it, and the mystic aura of influence and power which it radiated. It was the "noble metal."

In certain places in Europe, salt was available in abundance. Europe fully recognized its economic value. Europe recognized, too, that there was a certain mysterious quality about salt. It was woven deeply into the symbolism of religious and social structures. But it was not gold.

In the Western Sudan of northwest Africa, south of the Sahara Desert, a society had grown in a region where salt did not exist in adequate quantities. Gold was there in abundance. Salt, not gold, was the "noble mineral".

At the time of Cassiodorus, Europe's supply of gold, which had been accumulated over the ages, was running out. A large portion went to pay for the spices, fabrics, amber, furs, and metals of the Indies, Asia, and Scandinavia. Pirates and marauders seized much gold in their incessant raids on Europe's churches, cities, and the estates of the wealthy nobility. Quantities of gold were buried for security's sake.

Facing page: *The Arabian camel made possible the long-range, north-south trade between North Africa and the Sudan. A major portion of this trade was the exchange of salt for gold — a trade channeled through Timbuktu.*

While Europe struggled with the gold problem, several peoples of northwestern Africa worked out a pattern of trade that provided salt to the Western Sudan and gold to Mediterranean Africa. During the Middle Ages, at the very time that Europe most needed gold to develop manufactures, commerce, trade, and national states, African gold entered Europe's economic lifestream through a Sudanese border village emporium named Timbuktu.

The trade pattern was intricate, dangerous, guarded, secretive, and entrusted to only a few privileged non-European traders. The critical step, the direct exchange of the salt for the gold, was called The Silent Trade.

Europe's trade with northwestern Africa for ages had been short-range, largely coastal, on the Mediterranean fringe (the Barbary Coast). The inland hills rose to the Atlas Mountains. Over the mountains, the bleak, dry, hot Sahara Desert stretched 3,200 miles eastward to the Valley of the Nile. Its southward extent varied from 800 to 1,400 miles.

The Sudan (Land of the Blacks), a more fruitful part of Africa, began south of the Sahara. Trade into the Sahara from both the Barbary Coast and the Western Sudan was also short-range and limited. It was governed by the location and dependability of water holes, wells, springs, oases, and the availability of food for men, horses, asses, and oxen. The desert vegetation was sparse, dry, and generally provided inadequate food for the animals.

When the Arabian camel appeared in northwestern Africa early in the 4th Century A. D., Mediterranean Africa secured the means of establishing long-range trade with the Sudan across the Sahara. The camel normally carried a 300-lb. load without receiving water until the fourth day, even in the southern Sahara summer. In the northern Sahara, in winter, he needed no water for much longer periods. The camel thrived on the desert vegetation.

The most famous of the major caravan routes went from the northern edge of the desert in Morocco to Timbuktu, on the southern edge.

About midway on this route were large salt deposits at Taghaza. Black slaves dug the slabs of salt and loaded the camels. Generally there

In The Silent Trade, caravan merchants carried slabs of salt out of the Sahara and into the Sudan. This salt was profitably traded for gold produced by tribes living in gold-rich, salt-poor regions.

were 3,000 to 4,000 camels in the caravans. Crossing the desert was hazardous. Many caravans perished from thirst and from nomad attacks. A caravan round trip from Morocco to Timbuktu required about six months.

Timbuktu, established by the Tuareg nomads on a branch of the Niger River, became a trading center about 1000 A. D.

It was called "the port of the Sudan in the Sahara" and "the meeting point of the camel and the canoe." It entered legend as the source of the gold which the European traders secured on the Barbary Coast. Europeans tried unsuccessfully for centuries to find Timbuktu. It has been estimated that between the 8th and the 16th Centuries, Europe received an average of six metric tons per year of African gold.

Timbuktu produced neither the salt nor the gold for The Silent Trade. It profited from both, and channeled the trade.

Privileged Sudanese merchants guided the salt caravans to secret trading places. These required many days of additional travel beyond Timbuktu. There were several sources of gold.

Although the trade was well-established, the gold traders took few risks. They were well aware that the Sudan was a source not only of gold, but also of slaves.

They wisely avoided direct contact with the salt traders. The system used permitted the barter of gold for salt without a word being spoken, and generally without the trading groups even seeing each other.

A usual trading place was on a river bank. The salt merchants beat drums to signal their arrival. They arranged their salt in piles and went back out of sight. The gold traders then came out of their mines or caves with their gold and put the amount they were willing to offer beside each pile of salt. Then they went out of sight. The salt merchants returned and considered the offers. The process of bargaining continued until the salt and gold traders both were satisfied. Only then did the merchants collect any of the gold. They beat the drums once more to signify that the bargain was satisfactory. After the merchants had left, the gold traders came out and carried off the salt.

Sometimes the gold miners were in such need of salt that they were willing to pay as much as two weights of gold for each weight of salt. At times when they could not get any pure salt, they existed by using the ashes of plants, and by eating the meat and drinking the blood of such animals (and humans) as they could capture.

They knew from personal experience that they could live without gold but not without salt.

During the years of The Silent Trade in salt and gold, Timbuktu gained a reputation as a city of glamor and beauty. When the French explorer Rene Caillié reached Timbuktu in 1828, his mental picture of the fabulous place was shattered. Caillié wrote: "I had formed a totally different idea of the grandeur and wealth of Timbuktu. The city presented, at first view, nothing but a mass of ill-looking houses, built of earth." He found, however, that merchants were still amassing fortunes by importing salt from the Sahara.

The Sahara gold-salt trade had ended almost completely by the 1890's. But even today, caravans from Taodeni (the successor of Taghaza) in the Sahara carry salt to the village of Timbuktu.

—*William W. Boddie*

An Unsuspected Civilization

Europe knew very little about China until the end of the 13th Century. And then, when the Venetian trader Marco Polo came back from China in 1295 and began telling his stories, more than a few who heard him (and later read his book of travels) believed he was telling exaggerated traveler's tales.

In Venice, he was nicknamed "Marco Millions." It seemed incredible that his accounts of China, its people, its civilization, its resources, its industries, its vastness, and its wealth could be true. However, "Marco Millions" spoke from knowledge and experience.

Polo had spent 17 years in China, and an additional 7½ years traveling to and from that far-distant land. He spent a number of his years in China in the imperial service of Kublai Khan, the grandson of Genghis Khan. The stories which Polo told contained some errors and exaggerations. Yet on the whole, this most celebrated traveler of the Middle Ages presented Europe with the best information on China and Asia available in his time (1254-1324) or for four centuries to come. Then Europe began learning that China was almost impossible to exaggerate.

Europe in its Middle Ages hardly dreamed that China had been for thousands of years a great and unknown center of civilization, and that in many ways, China was considerably more advanced than Europe itself.

One notable person who took Marco Polo's book seriously was the Genoa-born ship captain, Christopher Columbus. Columbus used Polo's book as one of the key points in his presentation to secure the backing of King Ferdinand and Queen Isabella for his voyage in 1492.

Facing page: *The great and ancient civilization which had developed in China was virtually unknown to Western Europe until Marco Polo's monumental volume detailing his travels was written and published late in the 13th Century.*

Columbus was sailing west to reach Asia and its wealth—specifically to reach China, with a stop planned en route at Japan—when he discovered the West Indies. He died in 1506, still believing that he had reached Asia, and not a New World.

Among the fields in which China was further advanced than Europe was salt technology. The Chinese civilization had developed, as the other ancient civilizations did. where salt was readily available. The drawings on these pages give a few clear views of some of China's salt production methods in 1334 A.D. In that year, the commissioner of the government's salt administration in Hsia-sha Ch'ang, which was then under the jurisdiction of Shanghai, wrote a manuscript on the manufacture of salt. It was illustrated. The commissioner's name was Ch''ên Ch'ung. The manuscript, prepared from his own knowledge and from earlier Chinese works on salt, was entitled *Ao pó t'ú*, or *Pictures of Boiling the Waves*. The drawings have been attributed to two brothers named Ch'u.

Pictures of Boiling the Waves was included in a great encyclopedia prepared during the period of the Ming emperors of China.

In 1781, the Ming Emperor Ch'ieng-lung had court artists and scribes make copies of *Pictures of Boiling the Waves* for the seven Imperial Manuscript Libraries. The copies were made from the text and drawings in the encyclopedia. The encyclopedia itself was partially destroyed in 1860. The original manuscript and pictures on salt manufacture were among the portions of the encyclopedia thus lost to the world.

In the 1930's, the Harvard Yenching Institute acquired a rare manuscript of *Pictures of Boiling the Waves*. Pictures from this manuscript, reproduced on the following pages, are believed to be published here for the first time. They are practical drawings which show in excellent detail some of the methods and techniques the Chinese were using in Polo's time.

Marco Polo was keenly interested in salt.

Both as a trader and as a Venetian, he knew salt's value in commerce and in government.

On his long overland journey into China, he made notes about salt and other resources.

In Tibet, he saw salt being used as money. It was moulded under government supervision in cakes weighing about half a pound, bearing the imprint of the imperial seal. The Tibetan merchants took the salt to the tribes in the mountains and other remote districts, where they exchanged it for gold, musk, and other articles, to their own great advantage.

"For those people," Polo says in the translation used in Sir Henry Yule's vastly-detailed study, *The Book of Ser Marco Polo*, "besides buying necessaries from the merchants, want this salt to use in their food; whilst in the towns, only broken fragments are used in food, the whole cakes being kept to use as money."

In Yunnan, farther along his route into China, he referred briefly to salt produced from brine: "They have brine wells in this country from which they make salt, and all the people of those parts make a living by this salt. The King, too, I can assure you, gets a great revenue from this salt."

Polo did not say—possibly he did not know—that the Chinese had developed the technology and tools to drill deep wells for brine a thousand years or more earlier. They were raising brine from wells 1,000 to 2,000 feet deep in bamboo tube buckets. Students of Chinese science think that natural gas, found in drilling for brine, was probably being used as fuel to evaporate the brine two centuries before Christ. Bamboo tubes served as the pipelines from the well-heads to the salt evaporation works for the brine and the natural gas.

Farther eastward, Polo mentioned that great quantities of salt were made by leaching salt earth at a town named Changlu. "A kind of earth is found there which is exceedingly salt. This they dig up and pile in great heaps. Upon these heaps they pour water in quantities till it runs out at the bottom; and then they take up this water and boil it well in great iron cauldrons, and as it cools it deposits a fine white salt in very small grains. This salt they then carry about for sale to many neighboring districts, and get great profit thereby."

The evaporating pans were made of cast iron. The Chinese were using cast iron and deep-drilling at least a thousand years before Europe.

China's oldest known production process was solar evaporation. The leaching of salty ashes was another large salt source.

Before the year 2200 B.C., the Emperor Yu had levied a tax upon salt. Certainly salt is one of mankind's oldest and most consistently taxed necessities.

Polo marveled at the revenue which Kublai Khan secured from the salt tax. From the city of Kinsay [Hankow] and the territory under its jurisdiction, salt brought in "a great revenue," amounting to 80 *tomans*. All other revenue that the Great Khan received from the same area was 210 *tomans*. (A *toman* was 10,000 units of money.)

This revenue came from one-ninth of the Imperial Province of Manzi, the country south of the Yellow River.

Polo added a note of explanation:

"This province, you see, adjoins the ocean, on the shore of which are many lagoons or salt marshes, in which the seawater dries up during the summer time; and thence they extract such a quantity of salt as suffices for the supply of five of the kingdoms of the Manzi besides this one."

And he ended this chapter of his book on a practical politico-economic note concerning Kublai Khan's high regard for Manzi, the source of "one of the most enormous revenues that was ever heard of. And if the sovereign has such a revenue from one-ninth part of the country, you may judge what he must have from the whole of it! However, to speak the truth, this part is the greatest and most productive; and because of the great revenue that the Great Khan derives from it, it is his favourite province, and he takes all the more care to watch it well, and to keep the people contented."

—*William W. Boddie*

Top: *Seawater for salt production is pumped uphill through a series of pedal-driven square pallet chain pumps. The Chinese invented and used this type of pump nearly 1,500 years before the design reached Europe.*

Center: *The Chinese also obtained salt by burning salt-rich plants to ashes (lower right), then piling the ashes in a filter (at left) for washing with water to leach out the salt in a brine.*

Bottom: *In their salt technology the Chinese discovered different ways to produce brine which could be further processed to yield salt. Here a boatload of brine is delivered to a saltworks for processing.*

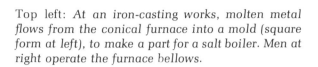

Top left: *At an iron-casting works, molten metal flows from the conical furnace into a mold (square form at left), to make a part for a salt boiler. Men at right operate the furnace bellows.*

Center left: *This saltworks is being equipped with a new evaporation boiler. The raised foundation will support the cast iron boiler—and in the space within the foundation ring, straw and wood will be burned to provide heat.*

Bottom left: *The cast iron segments of the bottom and sides of the salt boiler have been set in place. Now the cementers are sealing the joints while fires built underneath give heat for the sealing.*

Top right: *To feed the boiler operation, brine was taken from nearby holding pools, as at lower right— or from more distant points (upper right) by transfer to well-heads connected to the boiler by bamboo pipelines.*

Center right: *Constant boiling of the brine precipitated the salt from the solution. Then it was raked into piles and removed from the boiler for drying and storage. Meanwhile, fueling of the fire and addition of brine continued.*

Bottom right: *Now the salt is ready for market. At upper left, carriers load their boxes and baskets at the warehouse and then—under the supervision of officials—load the salt aboard a waiting boat.*

撈澱揀鹽

Wooden Ships,
Iron Men, and Salt

In the year 1453, in the storm and thunder of battle at Constantinople, the Middle Ages ended for Europe and a new age for the world began.

To the Ottoman Turks who took the city, under the command of Mohammed II the Conqueror, the capture of Constantinople marked triumphant victory for Mohammedanism in its Holy War against the remnants of the Roman Empire and Christianity in the East.

To the Christian West, which for seven centuries had fought sporadic Holy Wars against Mohammedanism, the fall of Constantinople was regarded as a great disaster.

The significance which history would later accord to the long-impending battle was less clear to those directly involved.

Out of the historic event, there surged tides and currents which influenced the affairs of mankind for centuries to come.

One of the great tides set off the European sea voyages of discovery.

These transformed the world. And salt, as well as Constantinople, was among the essential factors involved.

Salt's contribution was direct. Its ability to preserve meat, fish, and some other foods made it possible for men to carry food with them on long voyages. It gave men mobility. The knowledge of salt's preservative ability was not new. People had known it for ages.

Constantinople's contributions, both direct and indirect, were more complex.

Constantine the Great, the first Christian Roman Emperor, began building Constantinople in 328 A.D. as an expansion of an old Greek city, Byzantium. He said the location had been revealed to him in a dream. In 330 A.D. he changed the capital of the Roman Empire and the Christian Church from Rome itself to Constantinople.

It was situated at one of the world's most strategic locations, where Europe and Asia faced each other across the Bosphorus, the narrow, 18-mile strait that connected and controlled the major trade routes of its time.

Prior pages: *More inclined to trade than to exploration, Dutch sailors from port cities like Amsterdam made The Netherlands a major commercial carrier of both exotic and essential commodities — spices from the Indies, salt from European sources.*

Trade and wealth converged upon Constantinople from the known world. Constantinople was the terminal of the northern trade route by which caravans from the distant, unknown East and the "Indies" brought spices, silks, and other luxuries to the Roman Empire. Merchants from the West, particularly the Venetians and the Genoese, arrived by sea, carrying cargoes that originally were largely of salt and salt fish, but expanded to include other provisions and goods. The two other terminals of the Eastern spice trade — both parts of the Roman Empire — were Antioch in Syria (part of "the Levant") and Alexandria in Egypt.

As the city where many different peoples and cultures met, Constantinople became not only a center of trade, Imperial administration, religion, and theology, but also a center of learning, education, libraries, museums, literature, the arts and sciences, and the philosophies.

After the Roman Empire was divided in 395 A.D., with its western capital re-established in Rome, Constantinople, the capital of the East, continued its role as the crossroads of trades and cultures.

From its connection with the old Grecian city of Byzantium, it was spoken of as the Byzantine Empire. (The Christian Church followed the example of the Roman Empire. One part went to Rome; the other remained in Constantinople.)

The Byzantine Empire, where the Greek language replaced Latin, collected, preserved, and used the knowledge of the Greeks, the Egyptians, the Persians, the Jews, the Arabs, the Asians, and all civilizations of which it knew.

When the Roman Empire of the West crumbled under the barbarian invasions of the fourth and fifth centuries, its volumes of scholarship and knowledge were for the most part buried under the ruins of its civilization. The Christian Church saved some of them.

In Constantinople, the manuscripts were preserved. The Byzantine Empire fought for its existence against many foes, including three nomadic Mohammedan peoples — the Saracens, the Seljuk Turks, and the Ottoman Turks. It had survived, but barely, for eleven centuries.

By 1453, it had diminished from an empire to an outpost of the West and Christianity (and also from a city of 1,000,000 to a city of 50,000). Many of its scholars, foreseeing its eventual doom long years before it took place, had abandoned Constantinople, taking the ancient

Grecian and other manuscripts and scrolls with them to the West. They went mainly to Italy, on Venetian ships.

Constantinople, though only a shell of the city that Constantine had founded, still occupied its strategic position. It became the center of the Ottoman Empire and Mohammedanism.

Mohammed II and his successors were militant Mohammedans.

The spice and luxury trade which had passed through Constantinople to the Christian infidels came to a halt. Turkish ships soon swarmed in the Eastern Mediterranean. Western shipping dared not venture there. Within a few years, the other two terminals of the luxury trade with the East, Antioch and Alexandria, were also swept into the Ottoman Empire. The Turks expanded their domination much farther in the Middle East, Africa, and the Balkans. More than half of the Mediterranean coastline came under Turkish control.

The trade with the East, though small in tonnage, had been tremendously important to Europe. But the maritime nations of Europe were traders, not discoverers. They followed known routes of commerce, using charts of the waters they knew in their limited world— the Mediterranean, the waterways of the Black Sea past Constantinople, the shores and rivers of part of Europe, the British Islands, the Baltic, Iceland, a small part of the West African coast, and a few island groups.

Europe did not possess the ships or the navigational knowledge to go to "the Indies" and resume the spice trade. Even more significant, Europeans did not even know whether there was a water route to India.

What was required first was a higher knowledge of the world, particularly its geography, astronomy, mathematics, and history, than Europe had been able to develop during the Dark and Middle Ages that followed the collapse of Rome in 476 A.D.

The Byzantine scholars brought that essential knowledge with them. In Italy (and eventually throughout the world), the diffusion of this knowledge started the tremendous intellectual re-awakening that history knows as the Renaissance.

Cosimo de Medici, of Florence (1389-1464), famed in the history of banking and finance, was also a notable patron of the arts. When he decided to establish a library in his city, and include the works of the ancient Greeks and Romans, he discussed the project with a Florentine bookseller, named Vespasiano.

"He said to me, 'In what way would you furnish this library?' I replied that as for buying the books it would be impossible, for they were not to be had. Then he said, 'How is it possible then to furnish it?' I told him that it would be necessary to have the books copied. He asked me in reply if I would be willing to undertake the task. I answered him that I was willing," Vespasiano wrote.

"The library was commenced at once, for it was his pleasure that it should be done with the utmost celerity; and as I did not lack for money, I collected in a short time 45 writers [copyists] and finished 200 volumes in 22 months; in which work we made use of an excellent list, that of the library of Pope Nicholas, which he had given to Cosimo in the form of a catalogue made out with his own hand . . . And since there were not copies of all these works in Florence, we sent to Milan, to Bologna, and to other places, wherever they might be found. Cosimo lived to see the library wholly completed, and the cataloging and the arranging of the books, in all of which he took great pleasure, and the work went forward, as was his custom, with great promptness."

Some of the Greek manuscripts were works which concerned the earth — its size, shape, geography, its lands, its seas, and its place in the celestial system.

To the Europeans who gained access to these works, new horizons opened. Particularly important in the history of discovery were the works of three of the ancients.

The works of each of the three contained errors, as is now known, but parts of their information and philosophical speculations proved to be of significant value. The three were:

Eratosthenes of Alexandria (276-196 B.C.). He was in charge of the library of Alexandria. (That library, which was said to contain 700,000 volumes, was destroyed in later times. It is difficult even to speculate upon the unknown advances in civilization that perished with this library.)

In his maps, Eratosthenes introduced the concept of horizontal and vertical parallel lines to fix known locations in the world of his time. This concept was developed into the lines of latitude and longitude by later geographers, mathematicians, and astronomers. He calculated that the earth's circumference was 25,000 miles, and at the parallel which ran east and west through the Mediterranean island of Rhodes and the Pillars of Hercules (the Straits of Gibraltar), the globe's circumference was 20,000 miles. He believed that seas surrounded Africa on the south, and that the habitable part of the world's land mass, clumped somewhat like an immense island, extended east and west a little more than one-third of the circumference of the globe on the parallel of Rhodes. He thought the remaining distance was sea.

Pomponius Mela (who was living in 43 A.D.), the earliest Roman geographer. He was born in a small town on Algeciras Bay in southern Spain. Mela believed that Africa came to an end at a point where the seas (the Atlantic and Indian Oceans) joined, and that another continent lay farther south of Africa, beyond the place where the seas came together.

Ptolemy of Alexandria (about 85-160 A.D.). An astronomer, geographer, and mathematician, he was believed to be the most learned man of the ancients. Ptolemy accepted the calculations of an earlier geographer, Posidonius of Rhodes (135-50 B.C.), that the earth's circumference was 18,000 miles, and that on the parallel of Rhodes it was 14,000 miles. He also accepted the concept of another geographer, Marinus of Tyre (who probably was living about 120 A.D.), that the land mass of Europe, Asia, and Africa totally enclosed the Indian and Atlantic Oceans, which were like two vast, separated lakes.

Ptolemy's map of the world (A.D. 150) reflected the belief that the land mass of Europe, Asia, and Africa extended indefinitely to "unknown lands" and showed no sea passage around Africa to Asia.

However, he thought that the Atlantic was not too wide for a ship to sail from Europe westward to the "reedy and impenetrable swamps" of Asia on the other side.

There was also available in the Europe of the later Middle Ages a manuscript of a book of travels by the trader of Venice, Marco Polo. He had traveled overland to China and spent many years there. Part of his return trip to Venice had been made by water, from the Chinese coast to Persia. His travels had taken him through the very lands and islands of the East where there grew or were produced the luxuries of the spice trade that Europe wanted so desperately to find.

This manuscript gave Europe an unusually detailed picture of the East, its land and sea routes, and its resources. (It was written about 1298 A.D.)

More than 130 hand-copied manuscripts of this work, translated in several languages, have been found.

When the printing press was developed in the 1400's, Ptolemy's geography and maps were the first geographical works to be printed. Seven editions of Ptolemy were printed in Europe before 1500.

In 1477, Marco Polo's book was first printed.

Polo's travels across Asia convinced some people of influence that the Asian coast extended much farther eastward than had been previously thought. In addition, Polo had written from hearsay, and not from personal knowledge, of an island 1,500 miles east of the China coast called Zipangu (Japan). He described it as having inexhaustible sources of gold.

It was against such a background, that combined necessity, knowledge, and the conflicts of religions, that two persons succeeded in initiating the age of discovery.

The first was the Infante Dom Henrique, son of King John I of Portugal. The second, the son of a weaver of Genoa, was Christopher Columbus, who sailed for Spain.

Portugal had driven the Moors out in the 12th and 13th centuries and restored Christianity. In 1415, King John I of Portugal fitted out an expeditionary force to cross the Straits of Gibraltar and expel the Moors from their fortress city of Ceuta in Morocco. (To help supply this successful expedition, the Portuguese people of Oporto salted all the meat they had that could be preserved in this manner. They ate only the tripes of the animals. Today, they still refer to themselves as "tripe eaters.")

Prince Henry, with his father and two brothers, fought valiantly in that expedition. Thereafter, he dedicated his life to the advancement of Christianity and of Portugal.

Ceuta was Portugal's first base in Africa. It was one of the terminals of the old caravan routes across the Sahara into the interior of Africa, where the natives of the Western Sudan eagerly traded gold for salt.

In 1420, Prince Henry established a school or institute of marine science, navigation, and seamanship at Sagres Point on Cape St. Vincent, Portugal's farthest extremity into the Atlantic Ocean. He determined to make Portugal Europe's foremost maritime power; to find a sea route to the spice trade of the Indies around Africa; to find and assist the legendary Prester John, a Christian monarch believed to be somewhere in the world of the Mohammedans (the land was Ethiopia), in a fight to regain the Christian Holy Lands; and to extend Christianity further. Also, Portugal, all Europe in fact, needed gold.

Portugal's main resources were salt, wine, fruit, fish, and grain. It had no marine traditions. As a matter of fact, Portuguese seamen of that time would not sail more than six miles from land.

At Sagres, there remains of Prince Henry's marine institute only a large outdoor mariner's compass, made of pieces of stone set in the earth. But what was developed, taught, and learned there has been reflected throughout the world, wherever men have traveled the seas. He blended the ancient Byzantine knowledge with the best marine science of his own times.

He sought out and brought to Sagres men with the knowledge of the sea and its many arts from wherever they could be found (particularly from Genoa and Venice). Among the developments that resulted was the Portuguese caravel, a ship design that combined and improved upon the best sailing features of European ships of commerce and those of the Arabs. The caravel increased both the speed and maneuverability of ships, especially in making headway against contrary winds.

Prince Henry dispatched ships on many voyages—first down the African coast, then out into the Atlantic. Portuguese vessels under Genoese captains found and established colonies on the Canary, Madeira, and Azores Islands.

In a long series of voyages, often short in distance, the Portuguese learned seamanship and navigation.

They slowly worked their way down the west coast of Africa, establishing trading posts that also served as bases for additional voyages farther on. They brought back goods that Europe valued—ivory, African spices, black slaves, and gold dust.

By the year that Prince Henry died, 1460, the Portuguese had advanced down the African coast about one-third of the distance to the Cape of Good Hope, at its southern tip. The Portuguese had become Europe's leading seamen.

In 1460, Christopher Columbus was nine years old. No authentic portrait exists of this most celebrated of all natives of Genoa. There do exist several descriptions written by persons who knew him.

He was red-headed, blue-eyed, with a long, freckled face, high cheekbones, and ruddy coloring. He was somewhat taller than the average man of his time. He was affable, cheerful, optimistic, and moderate in his habits of eating, drinking, and dress. He was devotedly religious and zealous to spread the Christian faith.

Columbus was not for the weaver's trade. The sea, which was Genoa's life's blood, was his also. Columbus went on several voyages in Genoese ships in the Mediterranean. He was a seaman on a vessel in an armed Genoese convoy in 1476 which was carrying merchandise to Lisbon, England, and Flanders. Off the Portuguese coast, not far from Cape St. Vincent, the convoy was attacked by a fleet under French command.

Columbus, wounded aboard one of the ships of the convoy that went down, floated ashore near Lagos.

When he had recovered, he joined a colony of Genoese at Lisbon, then the maritime capital of Europe. For eight or nine years, he lived in Portugal. He made and sold marine charts, went on several voyages on Portuguese ships, and learned languages—Portuguese, Castilian Spanish, and Latin. He read books and manuscripts in these languages. He became a Portuguese captain.

During those years in Portugal, Columbus decided that it was not only theoretically but actually possible to reach the Indies by sailing westward.

As a matter of fact, he decided that he could find a direct sea route to the Indies that would require only a reasonable sailing time—and no long, impossible journey on which men would run out of food and drink, and starve.

He reached this conclusion after he had studied intensely all ancient and modern authorities he could find—the geographers, astronomers, philosophers, historians, and travelers. Marco Polo's book impressed him. He owned a copy, printed in Latin, that contained 70 marginal notes in his own handwriting.

The Catalan Chart (made by Jewish cartographers of Majorca in 1375), the best European map of the Middle Ages, used Polo's information.

Polo's book had impressed, too, an influential astronomer and physician of Florence, Paolo Toscanelli, who in 1474 made a new map of the world. It included information which—based upon Polo's book—extended the distance of Asia much farther to the east than any previous map. It showed the Island of Zipangu (Japan), erroneously, at a location 1,500 miles off the coast of the Asian continent.

Toscanelli urged the King of Portugal to sail west to the Indies. He received no favorable response. Later, Columbus secured a copy of the map and information from Toscanelli and used them to support his own plan.

Portugal, committed to the program established by Prince Henry, continued to progress successfully down the African coast. These voyages were producing profits, in addition to adding excellent marine charts and information of value to Portugal for future voyages.

In 1484, Columbus presented his plan and supporting evidence to King John II of Portugal. He had calculated that by starting at the Canary Islands, he would need to sail only five weeks to reach Asia. He used pieces of information from many authorities. Certainly he used Ptolemy, Marco Polo, and Paolo Toscanelli. Certainly he counted on reaching and using Japan as a base before going on to the Asian coast itself. Toscanelli also showed upon his map, on the direct route between the Canary Islands and Japan, an island called Antillia, which Columbus might find and use as a base. (It was placed on the map less than half of the distance to Japan.)

King John II, nephew of Prince Henry, referred Columbus' plan and his supporting evidence to his own mathematicians and astronomers. Upon their advice, he turned it down flat.

Columbus had seriously underestimated the distances to Japan and Asia, and neither he nor any of his authorities even suspected that the American continents and their connecting isthmus would block the route. Nobody involved seemed to have heard of the Vikings' discovery of North America about 1,000 A.D. As for the island of Antillia, it does not exist.

According to an intensive study made by the Harvard historian, Rear Admiral Samuel Eliot Morison, Columbus probably estimated the distance from the Canaries to Japan at 2,400 nautical miles and the distance to the Chinese coastal city he wished to reach at 3,550 nautical miles. Admiral Morison's study showed that by air, Japan's actual distance was 10,600 nautical miles and China's was 11,766 nautical

miles. Columbus just couldn't have made it that far over an open sea in 1492 without somehow renewing his supplies, especially food and drink.

Columbus was an extraordinarily persuasive man, an extraordinarily confident man, and an extraordinarily persistent man. Unshaken in his beliefs, he left Portugal and took his proposition to Spain, where he made influential friends. After eight more years of persistent effort, he succeeded in selling his proposition to Ferdinand and Isabella, the King and Queen of Spain, in 1492.

They provided him with a well-equipped expedition of three vessels and about 90 men. On August 3, 1492, before dawn, Captain General Columbus left Palos harbor on Spain's western coast. His flagship was a caravel, the Santa Maria. He went by way of Spain's Canary Islands. He replenished his supplies there, adding extra quantities of meat, bread, cheese, water, and wood. Repairs to one ship's rudder and other ships' work was done in the Canaries.

On September 6, the expedition sailed westward from the Canaries. They lost sight of land on September 9, and sailed over the open sea for 33 days. Land was sighted on October 12, and Columbus stepped ashore on San Salvador Island in the Bahamas.

He had sailed five weeks from the Canaries, just the time he had estimated to King John II of Portugal in 1484. He thought he had discovered the Indies. So did King Ferdinand and Queen Isabella.

Columbus, Spain's Admiral of the Ocean Sea and Viceroy of the Indies, made four voyages to the New World. His discoveries were too significant for the minds of the people of his time to grasp more than dimly. (The wealth that poured into Spain as the result of his voyages was easier to comprehend.)

But to the end (he died in 1506), Columbus believed that he had discovered the sea route to the Indies.

Salt passed into the folklore of Columbus and exploration in a story with a moral, published in 1565 in the first Italian history of the New World and recounted by Admiral Morison. The incident told in the story was supposed to have taken place when the Admiral had returned to Spain from his first journey, in 1493. It reads like this:

"Columbus being at a party with many noble Spaniards, where, as was customary, the subject of the conversation was the Indies, one of them undertook to say: 'Senor Cristobal [Christopher, in Spanish], even if you had not undertaken this great enterprise, we should not have lacked a man who would have made the same discovery that you did, here in our own country of Spain, as it is full of great men clever in cosmography and literature.'

"Columbus made no reply, but took an egg [hard-boiled] and had it placed on the table, saying: 'Gentlemen, you make it stand here, not with crumbs, salt, etc. (for everyone knows how to do it with meal or sand), but naked and without anything at all, as I will, who was the first to discover the Indies.'

"They all tried, and no one succeeded in making it stand up. When the egg came round to the hands of Columbus, by beating it down on the table he fixed it, having thus crushed a little of one end; whereof all remained confused, understanding what he meant: that after the deed is done, everybody knows how to do it; that they ought first to have sought for the Indies, and not laugh at him who had sought for them first."

Columbus had demonstrated that men could live aboard ship for long periods, could sail wherever the winds and waters would permit them, and find winds to bring them back again.

Vasco da Gama, A Portuguese Captain Major of Portuguese ships, found the sea route around Africa to India and the spice trade in a ten-month voyage in 1497-98. Portuguese who had access to the charts were forbidden to disclose da Gama's route under pain of death. The Portuguese became, for a while, the world's greatest maritime, commercial, and colonial power.

Captain General Ferdinand Magellan, a Portuguese who had served in the eastern trade but had renounced his citizenship after Portugal refused to pay him what he considered a just pension for the injuries he had suffered in its services, led the Spanish expedition that found the Straits of Magellan, near the southern end of South America, which made it possible to sail westward from the Atlantic to the Spice Islands. Magellan was killed in a fight with the natives in the Philippines, but one of his ships, under Sebastian del Cano, loaded with spice, completed the circumnavigation of the globe (1519-22) and returned to Spain. But Spain was more interested in the gold and silver from the Americas than in the spice trade.

Captain General Francis Drake, an Englishman, was the second circumnavigator (1577-80). He went through the Straits of Magellan and was blown south in a great storm. When the weather abated, he discovered Cape Horn, the southern end of South America and the second route from the Atlantic to the Pacific. He plundered immense treasure from Spanish settlements and ships on his voyage north along the American west coasts. He sailed far north, searching for a northeast passage around North America to the Atlantic, and when he failed to find it, turned back and spent a few weeks in San Francisco Bay. He then sailed westward to the Spice Isles, adding a few tons to his cargo of treasure, and continued around the world to England. Queen Elizabeth knighted him on the quarterdeck of his ship, shared the Spanish loot he had plundered, and the era of English sea power had begun.

Ships of many nations and companies endeavored unsuccessfully to find routes to the Indies by going northeast around Asia, northwest around North America, and westward by rivers and waterways through the continental masses of North America and South America and the Isthmus of Panama.

These explorations opened opportunities in resources and materials which were as valuable, or more valuable, than spices, gold, silver, or silks. An era of colonization followed, as the European nations learned the value of the New World.

The number of voyages actually made during the era of exploration will never be known. Only the successful have left records, and many of the successful ones were so poorly recorded that little can be learned of them now.

Columbus' first voyage differed from those of the Portuguese and those of other Mediterranean and trading nations. Their ships could come ashore to bases or cities or coasts and replenish their supplies. Columbus went out into unknown regions of the ocean and had no places to go ashore for food, water, and wood. (He had faith, though, that he would find the Indies where he believed them to be.)

Columbus took with him a year's supply of provisions. These consisted of salt meat, salt fish, sea biscuit (hardtack), cheese, dried chickpeas, olive oil, water, and wine.

Wood was used for cooking. The fire was built upon a bed of sand in a wooden sandbox. There was probably one hot meal a day, eaten from bowls, and likely it was quite salty in taste. The drink was wine, water, or watered wine.

On his second voyage, in which he carried colonists, Columbus requisitioned better provisions. He had concluded, as did many later colonizers, that Europeans needed familiar foods until they learned what native foods were safe to eat and became accustomed to them. He requested wheat flour, salted at the mill; wheat; hardtack "well-seasoned and not old;" salt meat, salt fish, cheese, wine, oil, vinegar, chickpeas, lentils, beans, honey, rice, almonds, raisins, and fishing tackle.

Ferdinand Columbus, who accompanied his father on his fourth journey of exploration to America, has left a vivid piece of testimony on hardtack when his ship was very low on provisions: "Our ship biscuit had become so wormy that, God help me, I saw many who waited for darkness to eat the porridge made of it, that they might not see the maggots; and others were so used to eating them that they did not even trouble to pick them out, because they might lose their supper had they been so nice."

English ships used salt beef, salt pork, salt mutton, salt fish, dried fish, hardtack, a few durable vegetables, and beer and water.

Marco Polo mentioned the basic diet at Hormuz, an Arabian terminal of spices brought by sea from India: salt fish and dates.

Unless they were thoroughly cured, meats and fish rotted. Heavy salting made them hard and durable, and certainly lessened their food value. Sailors carved such things as buttons and snuff boxes from the meat. But for centuries, there was no alternative method of preserving food, and the same salt diet was eaten on land in Europe and other parts of the world.

In 1835, a captain of the British Royal Navy anchored ship at Ascension Island in the South Atlantic and used some of the provisions provided at that British naval installation. "The salt beef had been salted in 1809 and could only be eaten, after it was boiled, by grating it with a nutmeg grater," he wrote in his memoirs. "The pork was little better."

It took iron captains, salt provisions, and wooden ships to make the great voyages.

But the shipboard supplies of food were, when possible, supplemented with wildlife, fish, and wild or native foods which were believed to be safe, or were eaten to prevent starvation.

On Columbus' first voyage, fish were caught. Vasco da Gama, on his voyage to India, caught fish, killed and salted down penguins and seals. (Another Portuguese explorer, running

short of food in India a few years later, killed and salted three elephants.)

Magellan's men caught and ate sharks crossing the Atlantic. They killed and salted sufficient penguins and seals on two islands off the South American coast to fill their five ships. In the Straits of Magellan, they found excellent fish (and probably penguins, seals, and wildfowl). Their food ran very short on their journey across the Pacific to the Marianas Islands — three months and 20 days without finding an opportunity to reprovision or rewater. They came close to starvation, and 20 died of hunger and scurvy. Like Columbus, Magellan had made errors in his navigational planning, but unlike Columbus, he was not lucky.

Drake's men killed 3,000 penguins in the Straits of Magellan and "victualled ourselves thoroughly therewith" — salted down.

In the southern Pacific, it was Spanish towns and Spanish ships that supplied most of Drake's provisions.

Sir Richard Hawkins, who went through the Straits of Magellan in 1593, described the reprovisioning of his ships with penguins: "They are reasonable meat roasted, baked, or sodden [boiled], but best roasted. We salted some dozen or 16 hogsheads, which served us (while they lasted) instead of powdered [salted] beef," he said.

Seamen with cudgels made circles around masses of the penguins and "ordinarily there was no drove which yielded us not a thousand and more. The manner of killing them which the hunters used, being in a cluster together, was with their cudgels to knock them on the head, for though a man gave them many blows on the body they died not. Besides, the flesh bruised is not good to keep.

"The massacre ended, presently they cut off their heads, that they might bleed well. Such as we determined to keep for store we saved in this manner. First, we split them, and then washed them well in sea water, then salted them; having lain some six hours in salt, we put them in [a] press eight hours, and the blood being soaked out, we salted them again in our other casks, as is the custom to salt beef; after this manner [of preservation] they continued good some two months, and served us instead of beef."

The natural and native food resources available to the discoverers and explorers were numerous and were found in enormous quantities.

These were preserved with salt which the ships carried with them, secured from natural deposits ashore or on islands, made by evaporating seawater or saline springs, or took from other ships. (Sir Francis Drake's first prize on his voyage of circumnavigation was a Portuguese salt caravel on its way to the Cape Verde Islands for a cargo. He went there with it.)

Salt provisions were not regarded as bad food by those who ate them. During the time when the famous secret diarist, Samuel Pepys, was in charge of the British Navy's victuals, the basic food was heavily-salted meat and hardtack. Yet Pepys wrote: "Englishmen, and more especially seamen, love their bellies above everything else, and therefore it must be remembered in the management of the victualling of the Navy, that to make any abatement in the quantity and agreeableness of their victuals, is to discourage and provoke them in their tenderest point, and sooner will render them disgusted with the King's service than any other hardship that could be put upon them."

Pepys himself loved good food, and devoted many pages of his diaries to describing the foods he ate. In his diary, however, one looks in vain for a mention of Pepys eating salt meat or hardtack himself.

As the voyages of discovery succeeded in mapping some of the islands and lands of the seas, trading ships and naval vessels put food animals ashore on them and planted seeds of vegetables and fruits to provide for future needs, when they planned to return by the same route, or to come that way again.

The use of the oceanic island and coastal stepping stones permitted the long voyages which kept men at sea many months and even years, and which came so soon after Columbus had cracked the egg. They were places where men and their ships could be renewed.

It was fresh food — meat, fish, vegetables, and fruit found at some such island — that sometimes saved enough seamen to bring home vessels that otherwise would have been lost at sea, when scurvy struck. It was the fresh food and its contents that cured scurvy, and not the "land and the land air," as many people of the world believed for centuries.

Later, some of these island and coastal stepping stones of the early voyagers became naval and military bases and colonies of nations, because of their strategic locations or resources.

The islands of Juan Fernandez provided a good stopping point for ships off the west coast of South America. Although Spain claimed the islands, until Spaniards remained there to keep others off, they were used by ships of other nations, privateers, and buccaneers. They had excellent water, wood, vegetables, fish, birds, goats, seals, and seafowl. Salt for preserving the food was readily available in the lagoons. In 1704, the captain of an English privateer quarreled with the master of his ship, Alexander Selkirk, put him ashore on one of the Juan Fernandez islands, and left him.

Selkirk stayed nearly five years on Juan Fernandez before he was rescued and returned to England. He did not use salt during those years on the island. He captured goats by running them down, and did not preserve their flesh.

Daniel Defoe, an English writer, transferred the scene of Selkirk's experiences to an island in the West Indies; and with his own fertile imagination, used these experiences for one of the greatest adventure stores of all time — *Robinson Crusoe.*

In the South Atlantic, St. Helena was a convenient island stepping stone. The Portuguese discovered and used it and built a chapel there. The Dutch planted fruits and vegetables. The English used it, too. The island had hogs, goats, fowl, game, figs, lemons, good water, and wood.

An outline picture of an "iron captain" (which a successful discoverer had to be), his methods of operations, and his major problems can be drawn from the study of only a few voyages. They are strikingly similar, though the discoverers sailed for different nations and in different waters.

He was a gambler — with great confidence that he would win.

He knew where he started from. He often did not know where he was going, although he thought he did.

He was an experienced, expert seaman. He used the best ships, the best marine knowledge, maps, and instruments that he could obtain.

He had the ability to deal successfully with kings and queens, the bureaucracies of governments and organizations, and with natives who were as treacherous to him as he was to them.

He knew that his suppliers likely would cheat upon the quality and quantity of food, drink, and ship's supplies they contracted for, and that his food would rot, his beer, wine, and water would become virtually undrinkable, and that he must always be searching for additional supplies.

He knew that where he found untested or unfamiliar food or drink, they might kill or disable all who used them.

He knew that disease would strike his ships, perhaps himself, and that he would not know the cause or the cure.

He knew that he would encounter perils of the sea many times and must handle emergencies successfully at once—fire, rocks, shoals, sandbars, currents, tides, storms, calms, or unknown phenomena of nature.

He knew that native peoples he would encounter were dangerous, but that he must use them ruthlessly, whether as coastal pilots, as gatherers of food, or as gatherers of the spices, gold, or treasure that he must take back as proof of his success.

He knew that the wear and tear of the sea would expose bad workmanship on his ships and equipment, and that he would have to improvise materials and methods to repair and save them, or he would never get back home.

He knew that he would lose ships and men.

He knew that any other ship he saw would probably be a pirate or another enemy.

He knew that his officers would often be unreliable, that his men would be the same, that sooner or later his capacity to command would be questioned, and he would face disobedience, desertion, and mutiny.

He knew that behind him his enemies ashore were whispering discrediting things about him in the ears of his backers and financiers.

He knew that only indomitable courage and resourcefulness would bring him back to home shores, whether in disgrace or in triumph.

Nonetheless, he went out to sea, an iron commander of wooden ships,
   —for fame
   —for riches
   —for Christianity
   —for patriotism
   —for trade

—and much later, to increase human knowledge.

Many nations sent out scientific and exploratory voyages, starting in the 1700's. These gave the world more oceanic stepping stones.

In 1835, one of the British vessels, H.M.S. Beagle, paid a visit to the Galapagos Islands, which Sir Richard Hawkins had been told of (but did not visit) in 1594: "Some four score leagues to the westward of this cape [Passaos] lies a heap of islands the Spaniards call the Isles of the Galapagos; they are desert and bear no fruit." Sir Richard sailed on.

The 26-year-old naturalist of H.M.S. Beagle, Charles Darwin, studied the volcanic islands and the life there from September 15 until October 20, when the ship sailed for Tahiti. The Beagle was on a five-year scientific voyage around the world.

The notes he wrote show he was fascinated by these islands and what he found there. Here are a few of them:

"This archipelago has long been frequented, first by the buccaneers, and latterly by whalers, but it is only within the last six years that a small colony has been established here.... The inhabitants, although complaining of poverty, obtain, without much trouble, the means of subsistence. In the woods there are many wild pigs and goats; but the staple article of animal food is supplied by the tortoises. Their numbers have of course been greatly reduced in this island, but the people yet count on two days' hunting giving them food for the rest of the week. It is said that formerly single vessels have taken away as many as seven hundred, and that the ship's company of a frigate some years since brought down in one day 200 tortoises to the beach. [The tortoises weighed about 200 pounds each.]"

While the Beagle went to replenish its water, he stayed on St. James Island of the Galapagos for a week with another member of the expedition and their servants: "We found here a party of Spaniards, who had been sent from Charles Island to dry fish, and to salt tortoise meat... While staying in upper region [of St. James], we lived entirely upon tortoise meat; the breastplate roasted... with the flesh on it, is very good; and the young tortoises make excellent soup; but otherwise the meat to my taste is indifferent.

"One day we accompanied a party of the Spaniards in their whale boat to a salina, or lake from which salt is procured. After landing, we had a very rough walk over a rugged field of recent lava, which has almost surrounded a tuff-crater, at the bottom of which the salt-lake lies. The water is only three or four inches deep, and rests on a layer of beautifully crystallized, white salt . . ."

He found the islands' natural history "eminently curious . . . The archipelago is a little world within itself, or rather a satellite attached to America, whence it has derived a few stray colonists [of bird, animal, reptile, insect, and vegetable life]." But most of the life upon the islands "are aboriginal creations, found nowhere else; there is even a difference between the inhabitants of the different islands; yet all show a marked relationship with those of America, though separated from that continent by an open space of ocean, between 500 and 600 miles in length."

The most remarkable feature of the Galapagos Archipelago's nature history, he wrote, "is, that the different islands to a considerable extent are inhabited by a different set of beings. My attention was first called to this fact by the Vice-Governor, Mr. Lawson, declaring that the tortoises differed from the different islands, and that he could with certainty tell from which island any one was brought . . . I never dreamed that islands, about 50 or 60 miles apart, and most of them in sight of each other, formed of precisely the same rocks, placed under a similar climate, rising to a nearly equal height, would have been quite differently tenanted . . ."

Yet it was true: of tortoises, birds, plants, reptiles. There were clear and definite differences that had evolved between the same species of life upon the different islands of the Galapagos.

Upon his return to England in 1836 from his voyage on the H.M.S. Beagle, Darwin began preparing his Journal for publication.

Charles Darwin's theory of evolution and his book, *Origin of the Species,* were profound fruit that came from the "desert" Isles of the Galapagos — stepping stones for voyagers seeking food, but stepping stones also for great advances in science and civilization.

—*William W. Boddie*

A Tragedy of Errors

When the Europeans of the Middle Ages and of earlier times boarded their wooden ships and set forth on their voyages of discovery and exploration, they knew that the winds and currents of the seas and oceans were taking them into many unknown dangers in addition to the perils of the sea itself.

The one single thing which proved to be the most dangerous of all was a disease called scurvy.

Today, scurvy is almost an unknown disease. Yet, for a period of 400 years or more, it delayed and changed the course of man's exploration of the earth.

It killed men by the thousands—suddenly, mysteriously, horribly. Nobody knew why.

One of the first symptoms—weakness, debility, and listlessness—was commonly considered to be laziness. It was even thought by some to be a cause of the disease of scurvy, and sailors were advised to be active in order to avoid scurvy.

The victim of scurvy could expect other symptoms such as these:

The bones and joints would ache. There would be shortness of breath. Then would come pimples on the legs and back, with hairs buried in them; redness of the skin and purple patches of blood on the skin and mucous membranes; black and blue spots on the skin, resulting from broken capillaries; broken blood vessels, with the escape of blood into the tissues. Hemorrhages into joints; heat, swelling, pain, fever.

The gums would become swollen, spongy, bloody, and sore. They would swell enough to cover up the teeth. The teeth would become loose, and could be removed by the fingers without pain.

Facing page: In the Mediterranean, British seamen found a cure and preventive for scurvy. But because they misidentified the vital element of that cure, it was later lost and scurvy's tragic impact was extended for centuries.

The feet and legs would swell painfully. Old scars and wounds would burst open. (Commodore George Anson, in his 1740-44 circumnavigation, lost one man from this cause whose wound had healed 50 years before.) Breathing would become painful.

The victim literally would "become unglued" —and he would die a painful, pitiful death.

There were dozens of theories about scurvy, dozens of "cures." But who could know that it was a food deficiency disease that could really be prevented and really be cured by a mysterious substance that came to be called Vitamin C, or ascorbic acid, when it was discovered in the 20th Century?

Through these hundreds of years, scurvy's negative effect upon discovery and exploration was tragic, and would be difficult to overemphasize.

On the other hand, the positive influence that the searches for the solution to the awful problem exerted upon the medical and nutritional sciences would also be difficult to overemphasize.

Many worthy and learned men, and many worthy and learned women, did investigate, study, and write about scurvy before its mysteries were solved and its prevention and cure were definitively established after the first World War.

However, this was not the first time that men had discovered the secret of preventing and curing scurvy. At one time or another, many individuals — physicians, surgeons, seamen, naval and military officers, businessmen, and students — knew how to prevent scurvy and how to cure scurvy. They did not know why that some things worked, although they often believed they did — and sometimes this had unfortunate consequences.

Indeed, the Royal Navy of Great Britain, which has become indelibly associated with the history of scurvy, wiped out the disease in the early 1800's — and then through an error in judgment or policy, lost the secret. When scurvy again became a significant disease in Britain's armed forces, they continued to use a worthless preventive and cure [preserved lime juice], and sought to explain scurvy's re-appearance in other ways.

Finally, in 1915, in the Tigris-Euphrates Valley of Mesopotamia, one of the early centers of western civilization, a British military disaster provided the clue that set the technologies of that day straight upon the path that led to the conquest of scurvy.

This is only one of the curious twists and turns of scurvy's trail.

Salt was one of the earliest suspects as the cause of scurvy, and over and over again, salt was suspected anew. [But some learned people claimed that salt would cure scurvy. Neither was right.]

Salt provisions were suspected. (But they were not guilty.)

Scurvy was no problem to Christopher Columbus. He left Palos on the western shore of Spain in August of 1492. His ships stopped at the Canary Islands to "refresh themselves," and then sailed westward for five weeks before they sighted the West Indies.

When the Portuguese explorer Vasco da Gama sailed from Lisbon on his successful search for India in July of 1497, he took four ships and provisions for three years. His was a longer and more hazardous journey than that of Columbus, as events turned out. He returned to Portugal in September of 1499 with only two ships and a third of his men. Scurvy was the disease responsible.

Early English voyages along the North American and Russian coasts did not produce scurvy. Neither did some of the early English voyages to Africa and Brazil. But in the 1550's, scurvy began appearing on English ships which went to West Africa for gold or slaves.

On Sir Francis Drake's circumnavigation in 1577-80, scurvy occurred. The "sickly, weak, and decayed" seamen regained their strength on an island in the Pacific when the bottom of Drake's ship was being cleaned and repainted with pitch.

Why did scurvy strike some ships and not others? Why did it afflict the crews of some captains on some voyages, but not on others? Why did it strike down men who seemed to be healthy and well fed? What caused it? What would prevent it? Was it a disease of hot countries and hot climates?

(We know now that scurvy does not show up in recognizable symptoms until the body's supply of Vitamin C has been reduced virtually to zero. Unless a person receives Vitamin C, this condition will normally occur between 160 and 170 days after the last of the Vitamin C was taken. We also know that when such people begin to receive Vitamin C, they respond dramatically in a short time.

England's Royal Navy began closing in on a solution when they became interested in the remarkable health records that Captain James Cook achieved on his three voyages to the Pacific, and the endorsement that he gave malt, or wort, for preventing scurvy.

Cook had experienced scurvy himself in 1758, when the *Pembroke*, of which he was master, had 28 deaths from the disease on a voyage across the Atlantic.

Officially, his first voyage (1768-1771) was to take a scientific party to Tahiti for astronomical observations and to explore the southern regions of the Pacific. But in addition, he was to test a new method advanced by Dr. David McBride (1726-78) to cure scurvy at sea "without the aid of a fresh vegetable diet" by substituting "wort, or infusion of malt" for fresh vegetables.

His ship, the *Endeavour*, was as well-provisioned for those times as the Royal Navy knew how, and included foods now known to contain Vitamin C. (The malt, or wort, by modern analytical methods, has been found to contain a "trace only.")

Cook was a great believer in fresh meats, fish, fruits, and vegetables. He supplemented his ship's supplies with these whenever possible, and while the *Endeavour* was crossing the Atlantic he had two seamen flogged for refusing to eat the fresh beef he had supplied.

When wild celery, scurvy grass, cress, greens, vegetables, or fruits were to be found, he had them gathered and served. He returned to England with no men dead or suffering from scurvy—an almost unbelievable record, for which malt received undue credit.

On his second voyage (1772-1775), Cook's mission was to determine whether or not a southern continent existed. He did further extensive work in hygiene and diet; and in a voyage covering more than 70,000 miles, he lost no man to scurvy aboard his ship. Again, malt received the credit.

On his third voyage (1776-1779), he was killed by natives in a quarrel on an Hawaiian beach.

But malt just didn't do the job, and in 1794, the Royal Navy authorized lemon juice for use in treating the sick and for ships going on foreign service. In 1803, it became standard issue.

Lord Horatio Nelson, another victim of scurvy in his younger days, was then Commander-in-Chief in the Mediterranean, with headquarters at Malta. It was to the Mediterranean that the Navy turned for the increase of supplies of juice it needed. Local suppliers (in Malta) quoted Lord Nelson a price of one shilling per gallon. London contractors offered a price of 8 shillings per gallon. The contracts were made in the Mediterranean. Nelson, who was allocated 30,000 gallons, requested permission to buy an additional 20,000 gallons for his fleet.

The results of using lemon juice were dramatic. At the Naval Hospital at Haslar, there had been 1754 cases of scurvy in 1760. In the year 1806, there was only one. Scurvy was still occurring on ships, but it was being cleared up at sea with "lime juice" which was really *lemon* juice.

The British Navy used the words "lime juice" and "lemon juice" interchangeably. These fruit juices came from the Mediterranean—from Malta and Sicily.

Within 50 years, scurvy was a rare disease in the British Navy. The "lime juice" was issued to the sailors mixed with sugar in their grog, or mixed with sugar if a man did not drink grog.

In the British Merchant Marine, where the juice was not issued, scurvy continued to plague ships. The issuance of lime or lemon juice, sugar, and vinegar was made compulsory in the merchant marine in 1844 whenever a crew had eaten salt provisions for ten days.

The use of the juice on British ships caused their seamen to become known to the world as "limejuicers," and "limeys."

In 1846, the needs of the Royal Navy had increased to such an extent that it was not being adequately supplied from the Mediterranean. It needed additional sources of supply, so on the suggestion of the Governor of Bermuda, limes from that British island were tested and found suitable for use aboard British warships stationed there.

Within 20 years, the British Navy had abandoned the Mediterranean lemon juice sources altogether and was securing all of its lime juice from the West Indies. A British company had organized lime production on the island of Montserrat. The fruits were gathered when they were at their most acid stage. The merchant marine likewise abandoned its Mediterranean sources and switched, to the extent it could secure the juice, to the West Indian supplier.

The tests that had been made on the West Indian lime juice's acidity were chemical tests, mainly to determine the amount of alkali required to neutralize a given amount of the juice. Over the years, it had again come to be accepted by many people that it was the acidity that was the valuable agent.

When the Navy and the merchant marine began using West Indian lime juice instead of Mediterranean lemon juice, the number of scurvy cases rose significantly — and no one could learn why.

The basic trouble lay in the variety of lime that was grown in the West Indies. It was a different fruit from that grown in the Mediterranean. It was the sour lime, botanically classified as *citrus medica acida*. The juice of the Mediterranean came mainly from lemons and some from a different variety of lime, botanically classified as the *citrus limetta*. *Citrus limetta* was a sweet lime, only slightly acid. (Tests made in 1917 showed that the West Indian lime juice possessed only one-quarter of the scurvy-preventing power of the Mediterranean lemon. The age of the juice, and the methods of preservation, were also factors.)

Faith in the power of lime juice faded out. Yet it continued to be issued in the British Navy and Army until after the first World War.

Certainly it was known that fresh food, particularly meats, green vegetables, and fruits would prevent scurvy.

The Royal Navy's diet had so improved that during the first World War, only three cases of scurvy were reported. In that same report, published in the Journal of the Royal Naval Medical Service in 1919, the Navy's lime juice ration was dismissed as having been regarded as useless for 20 years.

The British Army, like other armies that were engaged for long periods in the first World War, was not so fortunate as the Royal Navy. It suffered severely from scurvy.

The British Army, with a mixed Anglo-Indian force, invaded Mesopotamia in 1915 in an effort to push rapidly up the Tigris-Euphrates Valley and capture Baghdad from the Turks. They failed in this effort. A force of about 9,000 of the invaders retreated to the town of Kut-el-Amara. There the Turks established siege positions in early December of 1915. Relief efforts on the part of the British failed. Food began running short — a common occurrence in armies, as well as in navies.

The English troops were given rations consisting of 20 ounces of horse-meat, ten ounces of bread, and some oatmeal per day. The Indian troops, who could not eat the meat for religious reasons, were provided daily rations consisting of 10 ounces of barley flour, 4 ounces of barley, some *ghi* (clarified butter), and a few dates.

When the British general surrendered to the Turkish commander, 1,100 Indians were severely ill of scurvy, and 150 English of beri-beri. In the last six months of 1916, 11,000 Indian troops were disabled by scurvy in Mesopotamia. (The English horsemeat ration contained Vitamin C that prevented scurvy; the Indian ration contained Vitamin B-1 that prevented beri-beri.)

The Lister Institute of Preventive Medicine in London was endeavoring to find foods that would prevent scurvy and beri-beri. Through a combination of the nutritional research of Dr. Harriette Chick and her associates, and the historical research of Mrs. Alice Henderson Smith, some valuable and interesting information was published on the value of lime juice in scurvy.

Meanwhile, technology and knowledge was also being developed and pieced together at many places on the subject of "accessory factors of the diet," as one of the pioneers, Sir Frederick Gowland Hopkins of Cambridge University, first called them. Casimir Funk, of the Lister Institute, coined the word "vitamine" in 1912 (the final "e" was soon dropped).

The idea of deficiency diseases was not a new one. Dr. Thomas Trotter, physician of the Royal Navy's Channel Fleet, had written in 1796: "Whatever may be the theory of sea scurvy, we contend that recent vegetable matter imparts a *something* to the body which fortifies it against the disease."

Finding that *something* — Vitamin C in the case of scurvy — took a long time. Many people of many nations contributed.

In 1907, the Norwegian physicians Dr. Axel

Holst and Dr. Theodor Frölich of the University of Christiana, while doing some experimental nutritional work on the causes of beriberi, developed a diet which they used with guinea pigs. They concluded that the disease that the guinea pigs developed from this diet was "identical with human scurvy."

This was a key piece of research in providing clues for additional research on scurvy by many people. In 1927, a Hungarian named A. Szent-Györgi, working at Cambridge University, isolated a substance from animal adrenal glands, cabbages, and oranges which he first called "Ignose" (unknown), and then "God-nose"—two puns upon nosology, the science of medical classifications. He had difficulty in determining the structure of the substance, but later called it hexuronic acid.

In 1932, Charles G. King and W. A. Waugh of the University of Pittsburgh isolated some crystals from lemon juice similar to Szent-Györgi's "hexuronic acid" and identified it as Vitamin C. (Hydrochloric acid, derived in part from salt, was used in this historical work on Vitamin C.)

The same year, Szent-Györgi, then of University Szeged, and an associate, Dr. J. L. Svirbely, an American, cured guinea pigs of scurvy with their material—which they named "ascorbic acid."

In 1933, the two synthesized a pound of ascorbic acid crystals from the Hungarian red pepper. The technology was developed to produce the vitamin in any needed quantities.

Salt and salt water, so often called causes of scurvy, had been shown to have no part in either the cause or the treatment of the disease.

The reason for the success of fresh vegetables, lemons, and oranges as preventives and cures was explained. Additional natural sources of Vitamin C were found, as were better ways to preserve the vitamin's potency.

More recent research has developed further knowledge of how Vitamin C works as a factor in the formation of collagen—the connective tissue which "glues" the human body together.

The secrets of preventing and curing scurvy, greatest of the dangers that man experienced in the exploration of this world, have become his to use with certainty and security.

—William W. Boddie

The Irony of the Aztecs

The Aztec Empire, the most advanced civilization that the Europeans found in North America, rose and fell upon salt and legend.

The coincidences involved are amazing. They explain why the Spanish Conquistador Hernan Cortés was able, in 1519, to successfully invade Mexico with about 600 men, march through Aztec territory to the capital at the site of the Mexico City of the present day, seize the Emperor Montezuma II and his riches, and when driven out of the Valley of Mexico by a rebellion of the Aztecs, return in victory.

The Aztecs were one of eight kindred tribes of Nahua Indians who drifted into the Valley of Mexico in the 12th Century from somewhere in the north or northwest, seeking food and safety.

The Valley of Mexico, a vast plateau surrounded on all sides by high mountain ranges, lies about midway between the Gulf of Mexico and the Pacific Ocean. It is about a mile and a half above sea level.

The Aztecs arrived in 1186 A.D. and were not welcomed. They moved around the Valley and were beaten and enslaved for a period by another tribe. However, they were ferocious fighters, and soon they were slaves no more.

An ancient tradition foretold for them where to build their city and start their rise to power. In 1325, one of their chiefs saw the omen that the legend called for. He saw on an island in the salt lake in the Valley an eagle perched on a cactus plant which grew from the crevice of a rock. The eagle's wings were widespread against the rising sun, and in his beak he clutched a snake. (Today, that Aztec omen is the national insignia of Mexico.)

Facing page: *Grown in gloriously colorful profusion on the chinampas, exactly as they have been for centuries, these freshly-cut flowers are being trundled along the bank of a fresh water canal en route to market in Mexico City.*

The Aztecs moved to this island and one close by, built a temple to their war god, and did rise to power. The islands, which they connected together, are now part of the Zocaló, or Government Square, of Mexico City.

The lake covered nearly 450 square miles, about a quarter of the area of the Valley, during the rainy season. During the dry season, evaporation caused the surface to shrink and separate into five shallow lakes. There was no river outlet through the mountains, and the rains from time immemorial leached salt from the mountains and the plateau. This drained into the lowest and largest of the five lakes, Lake Texcoco, where the Aztec islands were. The water was too salty to permit agriculture.

However, one of the predecessor civilizations in the Valley had developed an unusual type of agriculture which the Aztecs used on the islands and which proved to be their instrument of power.

The chinampa system, as it is called, was already in use by other Indian nations around the lake where there existed powerful freshwater springs. These were principally located near the western and southern shores of the lake.

Chinampas were long rectangular strips of land laid out in regular patterns about 300 feet long and 15-30 feet wide. Shallow canals were dug on three sides of each strip, and the dirt and mud piled on the land strips. To prevent erosion, trees were planted on the water edges of the strips and stakes were also used.

The water from the springs irrigated the chinampas and at the same time prevented the intrusion of the salty waters of the lake. A nursery system of fertilization, seed planting, and transplanting was used. Water vegetation and mud from the canals were used as compost to renew the surface area of the chinampas between crops. It was possible to secure several crops a year from the chinampas. The food raised included grains, beans, chili peppers, tomatoes, and maize.

Freshwater springs of the necessary force existed on the Aztec island, and amidst the salty waters, the Aztecs grew food in quantities such as they had never known before and such as few peoples in the world were able to produce.

They employed the food as capital to maintain a standing army. They fought victorious wars with some of the Indian states around the lake and formed alliances with others, who found themselves subordinated to their partners. The victims included the Xochimilco nation, where chinampa farming still flourishes and where the myth of the "floating gardens" lingers on also. (The gardens never floated. They are ancient land reclamation projects.)

Soon the Aztecs owned Central Mexico and brought large territories into submission from the shores of the Gulf of Mexico to the Pacific Ocean.

One people that the Aztecs had fought and failed to conquer in the Valley of Mexico was the Tlaxcalans. They left the Valley, however, and established themselves in a mountainous region to the southeast. They lived by agriculture in the area of the present Mexican state of Tlaxcala.

The Tlaxcalans hated the Aztecs and had fought off their attacks many times. Like the Aztecs, they were ferocious and warlike. But unlike the Aztecs, they were not cursed by indecisive leadership and ruinous legends, myths, and traditions.

The Aztecs had adopted numerous gods of other peoples. One god, Quetzalcóatl, came from a preceding civilization, that of the Toltecs.

According to the legends, Quetzalcóatl had appeared among the Toltecs at the head of a band of strangers. His face was white. His hair was dark and long. He had a dark flowing beard. He wore a white tunic marked with crosses. The Toltecs considered him to be the god of air, representing the principle of good, and believed that he had given them the arts of government, agriculture, architecture, mechanics, and metal working.

Quetzalcóatl had left the country by sea for a land in the east, promising that one day he would return. The Aztec prophets had seen signs and portents that Quetzalcóatl would return in 1519.

Instead, it was Cortés and his ships who ap-

Facing page: *The chinampas, a productive and unique method of agriculture pre-dating the Aztecs, still supply food and flowers to Mexico city.*

peared. When they came ashore and established the settlement that became Vera Cruz, Aztec spies wrote reports which runners carried over the mountains to Montezuma in his palace on the island in the lake which the Aztecs called the Lake of the Moon.

The purpose of Cortés' expedition, which had come from Cuba, was to plunder the natives of treasure, to extend Christianity to them, and to increase the possessions of Spain.

Cortés had 508 soldiers, 100 seamen, 16 horses, and some guns. The Spaniards knew nothing about the Aztecs when they landed, but soon they knew a lot. The Aztecs required the payment of tributes from their subject peoples, and they held power by force.

Marching from Vera Cruz westward towards the mountains, Cortés was told much about the Aztecs and their riches. He had stumbled into a situation which promised immense fortune and fame if he played his cards right. And he did.

Montezuma was kept informed of Cortés' movements. He considered attacking the invader several times, but he did not. Montezuma was an indecisive man. Besides, he was bothered by the legend of Quetzalcóatl. The men were white, with long dark hair and beards, and they were advancing under the sign of a cross.

Montezuma sent ambassadors with gifts, including gifts of gold, in attempts to divert the Spaniards from their intention of visiting his capitol and himself. These gifts only made Córtes more determined to find and take control of the man who controlled such wealth.

Cortés' route led him through the land of the Tlaxcalans. He had been informed of the hereditary hatred which existed between them and the Aztecs.

The Tlaxcalans fought Cortés. He beat them. After this test in battle, they decided that through Cortés they might be able to secure revenge upon the Aztecs, and other desirable things.

In a letter report to the Holy Roman Emperor Charles V, who was also King of Spain, Cortés described the visit of submission to him by the Tlaxcalan captain general, Xicoténcatl: "He said that they had exerted all their forces, not only by day, but also by night, to escape being subjected to anyone, since at no time had this province ever been so, nor had they ever had, nor did they have, any master; on the contrary, they had always lived free and independent, since immemorial times, and had always defended themselves against the great power of Montezuma, of his father, and grandfather, who held that country (the Aztecs) subjected, but had never been able to hold them in subjection, though they had them surrounded on all sides, so that no one could go out of the country. He said also that they ate no salt, since there was none in their country, nor were they allowed to go to buy it anywhere else, nor did they wear any cotton clothing, because their country on account of its cold, did not produce cotton, and they were deprived of many other things on account of being so shut off. They had endured it, and held it as better thus to be free, rather than to be subjected to anyone; and they had wanted to do the same with me, for which reason, as several had already stated, they had tested their forces, and seeing that neither these, nor their artifices could avail them anything, had decided that, rather than die, and have their houses, and women, and children destroyed, they would become vassals of Your Highness."

Six thousand Tlaxcalans accompanied Cortés on his bloody march toward the Valley of Mexico. Among these were many merchants, going to secure salt and cotton.

The route led through the city of Cholula. The Cholulans, once friends of the Tlaxcalans, had since submitted to the Aztecs and were now enemies. The Spaniards and the Tlaxcalans held a massacre in Cholula and sacked the place. The Spaniards looted gold, silver, and featherwork; the Tlaxcalans looted salt and cloth.

Cortés met no further resistance on his way.

The city of Mexico had a population of about 300,000. The island on which it was located was connected to the mainland by three causeways. The Spaniards and their Indian allies came in upon one which was "two lances broad."

The city of Mexico and its wealth stunned and delighted the Spaniards.

Montezuma, accompanied by about 200 chiefs, met Cortés and they exchanged gifts. Cortés gave Montezuma a collar of glass pearls and diamonds. Montezuma gave Cortés two collars made of shells "and from each of the collars hung eight golden shrimps executed with great perfection."

Montezuma followed up these preliminary gifts "with many valuables of gold and silver work, and five or six thousand pieces of rich cotton stuffs, woven and embroidered in divers ways."

Montezuma then told Cortés that the Aztecs were not original natives of the country, but had migrated there under the leadership of a lord who had left the country to return to his native land, and that when he returned, the time had been so long he had been forgotten by the new generations. They refused to go back with him to his country or even to receive him as their ruler, so he left again.

"And we have always held," Cortés quotes Montezuma as saying, "that those who descended from him would come to subjugate this country and us, as his vassals."

Montezuma had mistaken the Spaniards for soldiers of the heirs of the legendary Quetzalcoatl, and this was a disastrous mistake.

Cortés put Montezuma under arrest and began reaping the treasures of empire. However, troubles came from Cuba and the Aztecs.

The Spanish governor of Cuba, under whose authority Cortés had organized his expedition, had been brushed aside by the Conquistador. Now he sent a large expedition to take over from Cortés.

Cortés hastened to Vera Cruz, took charge of this expedition, and brought most of the soldiers and horses with him back to Mexico City, where he had an Aztec revolt on his hands. Many Aztecs had wanted to fight Cortés.

They had been dissuaded. But the ruthless Spanish methods of control, including the captivity of Montezuma, inflamed some influential native leaders.

Top right: *In this chinampa scene, each block of soil has been fertilized and seeded, and will be carefully tended until ready for transplant.*

Bottom right: *Now the plants are being moved—by a canoe trip along the canals—to another chinampa for cultivation to full growth and yield.*

Mud dredged from the canals will be placed on the chinampa plots as part of the continual renewal of the soil and its fertility.

On top of that, in his absence, his lieutenant, Pedro de Alvarado, had massacred a large number of Aztec notables during a religious ceremony in their great temple.

Cortés found his men fighting in Mexico City and in serious peril. The reinforcements he had brought from Vera Cruz were not enough to crush the rebellion.

Cortés pressured Montezuma to attempt to calm the rebellion, but while the deposed emperor was addressing the enraged Aztecs from the roof of his palace, he was killed.

The Spaniards were forced out of the city in a desperate nighttime retreat, hotly pursued by the Aztecs. It looked like the end. However, the Spaniards were courageous and formidable men, led by one who was even more indomitable then they were.

The Spaniards called this disaster *La Noche Triste* — The Sad Night.

Cortés retreated towards Tlaxcala, although he was not sure he would receive harbor there.

But he was met in Tlaxcala by a force of 50,000 Indian troops, who were even then on the way to help him.

They had heard of the Aztec uprising.

Xicoténcatl, who had submitted to Cortés

when the Conquistador had passed through Tlaxcala, had spoken to the people from their great temple and urged them to kill the retreating Spaniards to appease the Aztecs.

One of the Tlaxcalan chiefs, Maxixica, threw Xicoténcatl down the stairs of the temple.

Maxixica told the people they had not eaten salt or worn cotton for many years until the Spaniards came.

They remembered. They supplied Cortés with troops, laborers, food, supplies, and ships.

And that is why Cortés was able to return to the Valley of Mexico to wreck, destroy and recreate upon the ruins of the Aztec empire the domain of New Spain—with himself as the Royal Governor and Captain General.

—William W. Boddie

The Big Casino

The United States of America, which has had such a profound effect upon world civilization, has been studied from many points of view.

But so far as is known, no one has looked at the United States from the frame of reference of a poker player.

The original name of the game of the European colonizing powers was the search for a direct cross-Atlantic sea trade route to Asia.

The game was played in a giant casino called The World. In the casino, there were many other games in progress at different tables. The poker table was marked "North America."

Spain was the first player to arrive at the North American poker table. She found no opponents there, and played some other games for a time at other tables in the casino. She won with encouraging regularity.

Another player showed up soon. This one was England, which had taken a seat at the table by sending John Cabot, a Venetian sea captain, on explorations of the Northeastern American coast in 1497. But not much play followed the arrival of this second poker player. Both Spain and England devoted most of their attention to the games going on at other tables—those marked "Europe" and "Asia."

The third player to join the game was France. Giovanni Verrazano, of Florence, had explored part of the North American coast for France in 1524. Unofficially, France's fishermen from Normandy and Brittany had been pulling some chips out of the pot, in the form of salt fish, from the fishing banks of Newfoundland, since about 1504. France ignored these fishermen for a time—she was too absorbed in other games even to notice the chips. But by 1524— only about 30 years after the game had begun— she decided to take a hand.

Other players arrived later. The Netherlands came in when they sent the English captain,

Facing page: *The mouth of the Hudson River, control point for a rich fur trade and entry of the water route to fertile interior lands, was a valuable card in the great North American poker game.*

Henry Hudson, to explore the North American coast in 1609. Sweden, arriving in 1638, sat in for a few hands.

The original cards used in the poker game, with the exception of the native Indians (so-called by mistake, of course), were marked "Made in Europe." They included political systems, economic systems, religions, geographical concepts, discoverers, explorers, traders, colonizers, ships, seamen, soldiers, guns, and gunpowder.

The chips included gold, silver, furs, land, salt, fish, timber, sugar, tobacco, cotton, potash, turpentine, tar, pitch, and others still to be identified.

The elements of chance were geology and geography.

The stakes in the game were gold and empire.

Poker may be, as it has often been called, the American national game. Like hosts of other elements of American civilization, however, it more than likely originated in some form in the Middle East, probably in ancient Persia, and travelled westward through 15th Century Italy to Spain, England, and France. Frenchmen brought it, under the name of *Poque*, into their Louisiana colonies in North America. Its outward forms, the numbers of cards, and the symbols on the cards, changed in its lengthy travels. The objective of the game did not change.

In North America, the English tongue corrupted the pronunciation of *Poque* into *Poker*. Poker enriched the English language with many expressive phrases and terms, including: chips, openers, the pot, ante up, raise the ante, sweeten the pot, check the bet, bluff, freeze out, pat hand, show down, busted flush, cold feet, stacked deck, deal off the bottom, above board, under the table, I O U's, and wild cards.

All of poker's strategies, techniques, and terms could be applied by students of the game to situations and events that constantly arose to test the skills and judgments of the players. For example, Col. George Washington of the Virginia Militia was rejected by the British for a commission in their Regular Army in 1754. He resigned his Militia commission and became a Virginia planter at Mount Vernon on the Potomac River. (He marketed salted Potomac shad and herring as one of his plantation enterprises.) Washington was a real "wild card." The poker players learned about that a few years later.

In the elements of chance — geology and geography — Spain was initially most fortunate. The Spanish found gold and silver in Mexico (and Peru) in staggering immensities.

The Spanish gained great wealth from the West Indian and Caribbean Islands. This was not in the gold and spices that Columbus sought so desperately to find. Spanish slaves grew sugar cane and produced molasses and sugar. Geography made the islands capable of producing many foods, and solar salt. Yet in time to come, the Spanish and other possessors of the sugar cane islands turned to the salt fish of the Newfoundland Banks and the New England coast for food supplies for their slaves. The salt fish which the Yankee traders of New England brought to the West Indies and the Gulf of Mexico for the slaves became another wild card whose significance was unrecognized for some time.

The great wealth that Spain gained from the New World shaped her policy more toward exploiting and protecting her possessions than in colonizing and expanding them. But Roman Catholic priests marched side by side with Spain's explorers and soldiers. The priests founded numerous missions, some of which developed into towns, such as: St. Augustine, Florida (1565); Santa Fe, New Mexico (about 1580); San Antonio (1718), and Laredo (1755), Texas; San Diego (1769), Monterey (1770), San Francisco (1776), and Los Angeles (1781), California. Only Roman Catholics were welcomed in Spanish territory.

The Spanish missions were generally established only after another poker player had strayed into Spain's holdings. The French Huguenots had tried to settle colonies in Florida in 1562 and 1564; the French explorer, La Salle, had put a fort in Texas, thinking he was in Louisiana, in 1685; the Russians had been in the California area as early as 1745.

For three centuries, Spain's mines in the Americas produced ten times the gold and silver that was produced by all other mines in the world.

In Spain's case, however, wealth did not equal power. She lost many poker hands in the form of treasure convoys to the ships of other players — England, France and the Netherlands. Their ships took treasures from Spanish American coastal and island cities. All three of them put colonies in the West Indies and the "Spanish Main." They smuggled slaves and did other illegal trading with Spanish possessions. (In time, they were joined by the growing New England fleet.)

France drew the next best hand to Spain's. And she played her cards well for more than two centuries.

The elements of chance—geology and geography—opened up North America to France through four waterways of destiny.

The St. Lawrence, discovered by Jacques Cartier in 1534, was the first. The second was the Great Lakes; the third, the Ohio River; and the fourth was the Mississippi River, the "Father of Waters."

Gifted with great explorers and great missionaries, France explored and used the waterways to develop a great fur trade, and, she hoped, the control points of a great land empire. The missionaries were very successful in converting the Indians to Catholicism, the state religion. Better than any other colonizing power, the French got along with the Indians. But the Iroquois did not like the French—an important exception.

At strategic control points on the waterways, the French built trading posts and forts. On the St. Lawrence, these included Quebec (1608); Fort Royal (now Annapolis), Nova Scotia (1604); Montreal (1641), and Louisbourg (1713).

On the Great Lakes, they included: Fort Frontenac (Kingston, N.Y.) (1672); Detroit (1701); Niagara (1725); and Toronto (1749).

On the Mississippi and its tributary system, they established Kaskaskia (1675) and Cahokia (1676) in Illinois; Vincennes, Indiana (1735); Natchez, Mississippi (1716); and a more southern Mississippi River fort (1699), 40 miles upstream from its mouth.

They also moved along the Gulf of Mexico to set up forts at Biloxi, Mississippi (1699), and Mobile, Alabama (1702).

In 1718, the French founded New Orleans on the Mississippi River. This city should have been the bluest of the blue chips that France played in the long-range poker game of empire. But when the show down came in 1763, Spain picked up New Orleans. It did not stay long in Spain's stack of chips.

France also overlooked another potential blue chip in her stack. In 1645, Onondaga Indians, one of the "Six Nations" of Indians that constituted the Iroquois confederation, had taken the French priest Jerome Lallemont to a salt spring on the shores of a lake in the Mohawk River Valley (near Syracuse, N. Y.). Another priest, in 1658, wrote a Dutch friend in New Amsterdam about this salt source. But neither the French nor the Dutch recognized the significance of this resource.

The Dutch, who were late in taking a seat at the poker table, drew strong opening cards.

In the elements of chance—geology and geography—they had better odds than they knew. Geographically, they occupied the most favored position for the fur trade except the St. Lawrence River. Henry Hudson had found the only river on the North American coast south of the St. Lawrence which was sufficiently long and navigable to support an extensive fur trade.

Besides the fur trade, Hudson thought the Hudson River could be the opening to the Northwest Passage to the Indies. On the basis of these possibilities, the Dutch bet more chips. They established a settlement in 1614 on Manhattan Island that became New Amsterdam, and founded trading posts for the fur trappers on the Hudson near the present sites of Albany (1615) and Schenectady (1661). They also established posts on the Delaware River (near Philadelphia) and the Connecticut River (near Hartford) in 1624.

Sweden was the next to enter the poker game. In 1638, the Swedes established a colony and a trading post on the Delaware River, to get in on the fur trade. The Dutch, in 1655, took the Swedes over. Sweden did not ask for another hand.

The Dutch stacks of chips on the poker table rose higher and higher from the profits of furs and hides, general trade with the Indians, and the carrying trade.

In 1635, the English colonists of Connecticut corked up the mouth of the Connecticut River with a fort, and squeezed the Dutch out of their trapping grounds upstream.

In 1664, an English fleet showed up in the Hudson River. New Amsterdam became New York.

The Dutch were frozen out of the North American game. Although they left the table, they watched the game closely and made side bets. They developed an extensive smuggling trade with the colonists of England, France, and Spain.

The Dutch side bets distracted and annoyed the English. The Dutch merchant marine had become foremost in the world. The English, striving to overtake and surpass it, fought three wars with the Dutch for supremacy on the seas. It was in the second of these that the English took New York.

The English, as mariners, traders, and colonizers, were strongly attracted to the northern fisheries off Labrador and Newfoundland. As they caught and salted down fish, they encountered numerous fishing vessels from other countries, particularly from France, Portugal, and Spain. The home lands of the French, Portuguese, and Spanish fishermen were large solar salt producers and fish consumers.

In 1583, Sir Humphrey Gilbert established the first English colony in North America at St. John, Newfoundland, in an effort (unsuccessful) to establish control of the Newfoundland fisheries. Ten years later, there were as many as 400 fishing vessels, from many countries, using the banks.

Between 1607 and 1732, the English established their original 13 American colonies on the Atlantic seaboard. The first settlement was put on the James River at Jamestown, Virginia, in 1607; the second was established on Massachusetts Bay at Plymouth, Massachusetts, in 1620. The last colony, Georgia, was established in 1732 as a frontier bulwark between the English colony of South Carolina and the Spanish territory of Florida.

England, unlike the French and Spanish, paid little attention to exploring and claiming other areas in the early years of the poker game. Also unlike her fellow players, she established no central administration, control, or state religion. On the contrary, the colonies became havens for religious and political refugees fleeing the persecutions and wars of Europe. They were Puritans, Catholics, Huguenots, Quakers, Church of England, Lutherans, Presbyterians, and others. For some years, they were neglected, even ignored, by the English rulers.

Far beyond the English settlements, in the wilderness, was the Appalachian mountain system. It extended from the present area of Maine to Georgia.

The Appalachians acted as a barrier to the westward expansion of the American colonists. At the same time, the mountains protected them from the Western Indians and the French. The French were moving down the waterways through the interior of the continent.

Some rivers flowed eastward through the Appalachians, including the James, the Potomac, the Susquehanna, and the Delaware. A few flowed westward, including the Kanawha, the Holston, the Watauga, the French Broad, and the Yadkin. These rivers wore a

few passes, or gaps, that later directed the courses of the American migrations westward.

The English colonists were tied to the Atlantic coast by another geological feature: they could not find adequate supplies of salt inland. They were dependent upon the sea itself or the imports of coastal ports for salt.

The Virginia colonists were producing solar salt from sea water by 1614. In the Plymouth Colony in New England, the colonists imported a saltmaker from England in 1624. He was a complete failure, "an ignorant, foolish, self-willed fellow," wrote Governor William Bradford. His saltworks burned down a year later. New England made several additional efforts to assure herself an adequate salt supply. As a region dependent on fishing to an increasing extent, she needed salt in even larger quantities than Virginia did. Finally she solved her salt problem by trade that involved the salt fish industry.

Access to salt was of fundamental importance in the location of new settlements in the colonies. Bishop I. Spangenberg, traveling with a group seeking a location for a colony of Moravians in Western North Carolina, wrote this entry in his diary on October 28, 1752, while in camp at the Catawba River: "Where? That remains to be seen.

"They will require salt & other necessaries which they can neither manufacture nor raise. Either they must go to Charleston [South Carolina], which is 300 miles distant. The distance is not the only objection—on the road they have mostly stinking water to drink; & are in danger on account of robbers. Or else they must go to Boling's Point in Va. [Virginia] on the James, & is also 300 miles from here. This is the usual course of the planters who usually require several weeks to make the trip. The roads are bad & there are many streams & bad hills to cross; or else they must go down the Roanoke [River]—I know not how many miles—where salt is brought up from the Cape Fear—but here there is no proper road laid out as yet."

In all colonial households salt was indispensable. In addition to its use as a seasoning, it was used to cure and preserve foods: pork, beef, game, fish, poultry, vegetables, eggs, and pickles. It was needed for curing hides and glazing pottery.

Despite the apparent handicaps of geography and geology, one of England's hidden cards turned out to be her system of colonization, so different from those used by Spain and France in the poker game. She moved slowly across the territory she had claimed, concentrating on developing the territory she had established claims to, through settlement, trade, and by limiting the areas in which her colonists were legally permitted to settle.

All of the English colonies initially developed economies based on agriculture, forest products, or the sea. Virginia's gold turned out to be tobacco. New England's turned out to be salt fish and the trade that developed from that start.

Two entirely different economies thus developed from the earliest two English colonies. Virginia's resembled to a certain extent the economies developed by many parts of the southern countries of Europe, and more especially by the agricultural sections of England. New England's followed in many ways the pattern developed centuries earlier in Venice and later in Holland—trade, based on salt fish.

Captain John Smith, a shrewd and outstanding participant in America's early history, explored the New England coast in 1614. In his book, *Generall Historie of Virginia, New England, and the Summer Isles, 1584-1624*, he described the great fish resources of New England as potential sources of wealth for colonists. He added some sound advice, in these words: "Let not the meanness of the word Fish distaste you, for it will afford as good gold as the mines of Guinea [the African source of Portugal's gold] and Potośi [in Spanish Peru] with less hazard and charges, and more certainty and facility."

The New Englanders built ships from their timber resources and went to the fisheries. They secured their salt by barter with the fishing boats of France, Spain, and Portugal. These boats brought the solar salt from their home lands to preserve their own catches to take back to Europe, and also to use as ballast on their outward voyages to the Labrador and Newfoundland fisheries. The Yankees developed a far-flung trade in salt fish, salt meats, hides, and timber products, with England, other American colonies, and the West Indies.

The Navigation Ordinance which England had passed in its show down game with the Dutch, in 1651, required that all goods imported into England or English colonies had to be carried in English-built and English-manned ships. (*English* meant English colonials as well.)

The New England shipbuilding industry boomed, and the trading activities increased.

In 1660, England began borrowing parts of the system of play which had been used with apparent success by her fellow poker players since they first joined the game. She put into effect another trade-control act which "enumerated" certain commodities that her colonies could export only to England. The "enumerated" articles were sugars, tobacco, cotton, wool, indigo, fustick or other dye-ing woods. Other items were added in various later acts. (Colonial tobacco had already been made an English mother-country monopoly in 1624.)

The principal non-enumerated trade commodities of the time, which England had no need of and did not wish to handle, were salt meats, salt fish, rum, and grain. They could be exported anywhere except to England.

The Yankee traders took these "non-enumerated" commodities and others—barrel staves, hides, lumber, horses, and foods—to the West Indies. Horses, as well as slaves, were needed to work the sugar cane plantations. The British islands became good customers. So did the Spanish, Dutch, and French colonies. The New Englanders loaded return cargoes which included sugar, dyewoods, other "enumerated" articles, molasses, and rum.

In 1663, England enacted another Navigation Act which prohibited, through the means of very high customs duties, anything grown, produced, or manufactured in Europe from being shipped to England's colonies unless it was loaded in England aboard an English-built and English-manned ship.

But these specific exceptions were listed: salt produced in any part of Europe for the fisheries of New England and Newfoundland; Madeira wines and Azores wines; and victuals, horses, and servants of Scotch and Irish origin loaded in Scotland and Ireland. New York and Pennsylvania, in 1727, were given exceptions for salt to be used in their fisheries.

The Yankees had extended their trade in salt fish and barrel staves across the Atlantic to the Azores and Madeira Islands, and to Portugal and Spain. All of these places were producers of solar salt and of wine. The New England ships brought back mixed cargoes of salt and Canary, Madeira, Portuguese, and Spanish wines. Often they smuggled in forbidden goods.

As a result of the Navigation Act of 1663, the New Englanders developed "triangular trade" routes that sometimes included stops in England, and sometimes bypassed England altogether. In one of these bypass trades, the Yankees distilled the molasses, for which they had traded salt fish in the West Indies, and took cargoes of rum to Africa. They traded the rum for slaves, which they carried to the West Indies and traded for more molasses and coins or bills of exchange. The money was used in legal trade with England for needed goods that could not be secured otherwise—in the main, from smuggling.

England continued to play by the Spanish-French-Dutch system. She attempted to apply stricter rules and regulations to control trade, so that the colonists would be producers of raw materials only, and consumers of English-exported goods. England particularly wanted to stop the trade with the Spanish, French, and Dutch colonies in the West Indies. Her own West Indian islands were being hurt by the competition in selling molasses.

Thus England, who started shuffling the cards for a game with the Dutch, found herself becoming involved in a new side game with her American colonies.

But before this game became deadly serious, England and her colonies joined to play a show down game with France. This game started with gunshots in the Ohio River Valley in 1754.

Both England and France claimed this valley, and both needed it for trade and colonization. The French, especially, needed it for a communication line by water between their Canadian and Louisiana territories, particularly New Orleans.

The French Governor General of Canada, the Marquis DuQuesne, began in 1753 building a line of forts south from Lake Erie to secure this route. Two were built near the present sites of Erie and Waterford, Pa., and a third was made from a captured English trading post located at the present site of Franklin, Pa.

Lieutenant Governor Robert Dinwiddie of Virginia learned of these French forts and sent 21-year-old Major George Washington of the Virginia Militia, with six men, a guide, and an interpreter, to warn the French to leave the Ohio Valley. The French ignored the warning. Instead they seized a fort that another group of Virginians had begun building at the forks of the Ohio (Pittsburgh, Pa.) and rebuilt it themselves, naming it Fort DuQuesne.

Virginia reacted further by sending 300 militiamen, with Washington second in command, to reinforce the party building the English fort, not knowing the French had taken it.

On May 27, 1754, Lt. Col. Washington, with 60 men, attacked and defeated a smaller French force which had advanced about 45 miles southeast of Fort DuQuesne.

Washington's attack in that remote Pennsylvania glen started the French and Indian War, as it is known in America, or the Seven Years War, as it is known in Europe.

The war spread from the wilderness to the other colonies, to Canada, to Europe, India, the Philippines, the African coast, and the West Indies. In addition to assistance from the American colonists, England received help from Frederick the Great of Prussia. Spain became an ally of France, as did Austria, Russia, Sweden, and Saxony.

The casino was busy.

The Marquis DuQuesne attempted to secure the aid of the powerful Iroquois Indians, who occupied the strategic valleys of upper New York that led through the Appalachian range. The Iroquois territory included the only extensive salt resources (near Syracuse, N.Y.) then known to exist in the British Atlantic colonies.

Most of the Iroquois had hated the French since 1609. In that year, Samuel de Champlain, the first French Governor General of Canada and a noted explorer, had joined the Algonquin Indians in an attack on the Iroquois in the vicinity of Lake Champlain. Champlain used his gun, and two Indians fell dead. The terrified Iroquois, who had never heard gunpowder before, had fled. Those fateful bullets fired by Champlain became disastrous cards for France.

Years later, DuQuesne said to the Iroquois: "Are you ignorant of the difference between the King of England and the King of France? Go see the forts that our King has established and you will see that you can still hunt under their very walls. They have been placed for your advantage in places which you frequent. The English, on the contrary, are no sooner in possession of a place than the game is driven away. The forest falls before them as they advance, and the soil is laid bare so that you can scarce find the wherewithal to erect a shelter for the night."

DuQuesne had used a blue chip. The Iroquois, who had fought beside the English in earlier clashes with the French and their Indian allies, sat out the French and Indian War as neutrals.

Even so, when the war ended in 1763, the French were out of the game in North America. The British permitted the French to keep two islands off the southern coast of Newfoundland, St. Pierre and Miquelon, to use as shore bases for their fishermen, permitted them to continue to use the fisheries, and permitted them to dry fish ashore on parts of Newfoundland.

England took possession of Canada and all other French territory east of the Mississippi, with one exception. That was New Orleans.

Spain got New Orleans and all French possessions and claims west of the Mississippi. Spain swapped Florida to England for the return of Havana, which the British had captured in 1762. Spain also gave up her rights to use the fisheries off Labrador and Newfoundland.

England had become the big winner.

It looked like a new deck and a new deal. It was. But at the table now were the unasked and unwanted new players who had been playing in the side game with England — the British colonies of the Atlantic seaboard.

—William W. Boddie

The Game
Moves West

England, the big winner in the first 270 years of The Great North American Poker Game, now began playing her cards so badly with her North American colonies that in 20 years she lost them.

In 1763, the same year that the French and Indian War was concluded, George III, King of England (also Duke of Hanover and Luneburg), issued a proclamation forbidding the American colonists from settling beyond the divide of the Appalachian Mountains.

The apparent reason for the new colonization policy was England's desire to avoid trouble with the Indians, and to settle the new western lands gradually and in an orderly manner.

But a report to the British Board of Trade (in 1772) summarized the basic reasons bluntly: "The object of colonization in North America has been to improve and extend the commerce, navigation, and manufactures of this Kingdom — 1) by the fisheries on the northern coast; 2) by the growth of naval stores [tar, pitch, turpentine, shipbuilding lumber] and raw produce to be exchanged for manufactures and other merchandize; 3) by securing a supply of lumber and provisions [salt meat, salt fish, grains] for the island colonies [in the British West Indies]. For these purposes, settlements were confined as much as possible to the seacoast, so as to be accessible to merchant ships and defensible by the British Navy, which could use the ports as stations in time of war."

The colonists ignored King George's proclamation and moved on through the Appalachians. Some settlements had already been made there before the proclamation was issued.

The early westward movements came chiefly from the colonies of North Carolina, Virginia, Maryland, and Pennsylvania.

Facing page: *Spain, Mexico, England, France, and Russia — to varying degrees and at different times — held or claimed lands in what is now that vast expanse of the United States from the Mississippi River to San Francisco and the Pacific Ocean.*

The southern route went through the Cumberland Gap in the Alleghenies (located where the present states of Kentucky, Tennessee, and Virginia meet). Daniel Boone, the most famous of America's early frontiersmen, tracked the Wilderness Road through this gap, and following rivers, Indian trails, and paths worn by the feet of buffalo, went to the bluegrass lands of Kentucky. He found fertile lands, good hunting, and salt-brine springs and licks. He established Boonesborough.

Another branch of the Wilderness Road went by way of Crab Orchard and Bullitt's Lick, which was to become a center for supplying the frontier communities from the Ohio to the Cumberland Rivers with salt.

James Robertson went through the Cumberland Gap and followed buffalo traces southwestward to salt licks and water. He established the settlement that became Nashville, Tennessee, on the Cumberland River.

Some Virginia colonists went westward through the Potomac and the Great Kanawha River Valleys. Salt brines were found in the valleys of the Holston and the Great Kanawha Rivers. During the American Civil War (1861-65) these brines became significant cards to both the North and the South.

At Pittsburgh (formerly Fort DuQuesne) three routes met: two from Philadelphia and one from Cumberland, Maryland. From Pittsburgh, the Ohio River was the major route of colonization. The transportation was canoes, flatboats, and rafts.

The area of heaviest early settlement lay between the Ohio and the Tennessee Rivers, which not only had few Indian settlements, but was far enough from the lands claimed by the French on the north and the Spanish on the south to permit relatively peaceful infiltration by English colonists. The states of Kentucky and Tennessee developed in this area. They were the first states west of the Appalachian Mountains to join the new United States of America—in 1792 and 1796.

In 1764, England tried to stop the salt fish-sugar-molasses-rum trade of the colonists with the French, Dutch, and Spanish in the West Indies. She played numerous other bad cards in attempting to control and tax the colonial trade in the next few years. The worst trouble for the colonists came when the British began enforcing these laws. In previous times, British officials had often closed their eyes or turned their backs to avoid seeing violations of unpopular or unreasonable laws.

The result? "The colonists," wrote the economist David A. Wells, "were a nation of law-breakers; nine-tenths of the colonial merchants were smugglers. One-quarter of the whole number of the signers of the Declaration of Independence were bred to the contraband trade. John Hancock [whose oversized signature stands out most boldly on that document] was the prince of contraband traders and, with John Adams [second President of the United States] as his counsel, was on trial before the Admiralty Court in Boston at the exact hour of the shedding of blood at Lexington [the start of the American War of Independence], to answer for half a million dollars' penalties alleged to have been by him incurred as a smuggler."

George Washington, the wild card that the British had discarded back in the French and Indian War, turned up as Commander-in-Chief of the American and French forces that won the War of Independence for America (1776-1783). He became the first President of the United States.

During the American Revolution, salt was in short supply. To overcome the "salt famine," the states offered bounties to salt makers. Many small salt boiling operations were set up along the coast. The British raided and destroyed them whenever they could. Agents of the Continental Congress abroad tried to get salt aboard ships sailing to North America from Europe and the West Indies. A shipload of British salt was captured. The British captured General Washington's salt supply before the battle of Brandywine. Salt was treasured.

After the war, the nation grew. Commerce followed the frontiersmen down the rivers and through the mountains.

"The people in Pittsburgh, and the western country along the waters of the Ohio, draw their supplies from Philadelphia and Baltimore; but they send the productions of the country, which would be too bulky for land carriage, down the Ohio and Mississippi to New Orleans," an English traveller wrote in 1795. "On an average, it takes about 28 days to go down there with the stream; but to return by water it takes from 60 days to three months ... They seldom think of bringing back boats which are sent down from Pittsburgh, but on arriving at New Orleans they are broken up and the planks sold ... The men get back the best way they can, generally in ships bound from New Orleans to southern states, and from thence home by land."

Another English traveller a few years later listed the principal river trade as flour, corn, salt, cider, apples, live hogs, bacon, glass, and earthenware. He wrote that barter was used to a large extent, since money was scarce.

"I rode an excellent horse to the head of the waters; and finding him of no further use from my having to take boat there, I proposed selling him to the highest bidder," he reported. "I was offered in exchange for him salt, flour, hogs, land, cast-iron salt pans, Indian corn, whiskey—in short, everything but what I wanted, which was money. The highest offer made was cast-iron salt-pans to the amount of $120. I asked the proprieter of this heavy commodity how much cash he would allow me instead of such an encumbrance; his answer was, without any shame or hesitation, $40 at most. I preferred the pans."

In 1800, prices of salt in the "new west" ranged from $3 per bushel in Kentucky, to $5 per bushel in western Virginia, to $10 per bushel at Pittsburgh, and as high as $16 in Ohio.

In 1807, Robert Fulton's steamboat went into service on the Hudson River. Four years later, the first steamboat on western waters went from Pittsburgh down the Ohio and Mississippi to New Orleans.

Many eastern states and cities talked over plans for canals and railroads to move in on the Mississippi River trade and break the ace cards that nature and France had dealt New Orleans, making that city the middleman of a continent.

New York State was the first who did it. She built the Erie Canal from the Hudson River north of Albany to Buffalo on Lake Erie. The canal was 364 miles long, cost more than $7,000,000, and was completed in 1825.

The Erie Canal made New York City the world port of the United States and the main port of entry for immigrants. The canal tied the American Northeast, Midwest, and Northwest together. Soon other canals, railroads, and roads strengthened these ties.

The Erie Canal was 40 feet wide, four feet deep, and had 88 locks. Horses and mules, hitched to the canal boats, pulled them. The boat traffic went two ways, bringing out goods from the midcontinent, carrying in goods from the world.

A tax of 12½ percent on New York state salt helped build the canal; and this tax, plus the tolls charged on the salt shipped on it, paid nearly half of the construction costs.

The route of the canal passed through Syracuse, the center of the New York salt industry. In 1788, New York had made a treaty with the Indians and taken over the salt reserves as a state property.

"Previous to the construction of the Erie Canal, the cost of transporting a ton of merchandize of produce from the City of New York to the City of Buffalo was $100. The time required was 20 days!" wrote a transportation authority in 1868. "Upon the opening of the Canal, the cost of transportation from Buffalo to New York was reduced from $100 to $5 per ton, and the time from 20 to six days."

The Mississippi River and New Orleans were in the cards that brought the French back into the game for a few hands for high stakes in 1800. France's player was Napoleon Bonaparte, First Consul of the Empire that he formed out of the destruction of the "Old Regime" in the French Revolution (1789).

The dealer, however, was Thomas Jefferson, third President of the United States. The cards flew fast in this game. Napoleon had Spain secretly transfer back to France the territorial claims west of the Mississippi, plus New Orleans, that France had ceded to Spain in the treaty of 1763 at the end of the French and Indian War.

of New Orleans. The British lost. In another game they were playing at the same time with the Emperor Napoleon, the British won at Waterloo.

As it had been in the American Revolution, salt was scarce in the War of 1812. The British destroyed many salt boiling operations on the American coasts. The need for a strategic interior water route for salt, not so easily attacked from the ocean and the lakes, was one of the factors involved in building the Erie Canal.

Spain was having problems with her North American cards. Her Mexican provinces had begun to revolt in 1810, and were winning more hands than they lost. Spain continued to bluff, but she knew her cards were getting poorer.

Several military expeditions, originating in the United States and including its citizens, invaded Spanish territory to help Mexico fight against Spain—or so it was claimed.

The United States until 1819 claimed that the Louisiana Purchase lands extended to the Rio Grande, and thus included Texas. In 1819, there was a swap. Spain transferred Florida and the Spanish claims to the Oregon territories to the United States. The United States gave up her claim to Texas, between the Sabine River and the Rio Grande.

In 1820, Spain changed her tactics. There was no gold or silver in Texas. But in order to start settling the country, she gave permission to Moses Austin to establish a colony there. She required that the colonists must be Roman Catholics and Spanish citizens. Austin, as a resident of Missouri, had been a Spanish citizen before the Louisiana Purchase.

The next year, Mexico succeeded in establishing her independence from Spain. She took over the rest of Spain's chips and her seat at the poker table. England, with a much-reduced pile of chips, was the only one of the original three North American players left. The other two players now at the table were the United States and the Republic of Mexico.

In 1823, the Central American states declared their independence from Mexico and soon set up separate republics. Occasionally, after that, they became involved in the game, but were never steady players.

Russia, the potential player who had come in at the back door in 1741, had not yet accumulated enough chips to get a seat at the table. But her presence had not gone unnoticed. In 1824, the United States negotiated a treaty with Russia whereby Russia abandoned her claims south of the latitude of 54 degrees, 40 minutes (a line now in Canada). The following year, England made a treaty which gave her title to the Russian claims north of that line except for Alaska. It was not until 1867, when Russia sold Alaska to the United States, that she was completely out of the North American poker game.

Americans from the United States rapidly moved into Texas. They adopted the Roman Catholic religion and swore allegiance to Mexico. (There were many baptisms.) Mexico continued the Spanish system of military rule in her remote province of Texas, and established forts there.

The Texans were generally satisfied with the conditions they found in their new land. One of their earliest industrial establishments was a saltworks at Velasco, at the mouth of the Brazos River, near one of the Mexican forts.

But they soon grew tired of military rule and the frequent upheavals in the government of the Republic of Mexico.

The Texans began to revolt in 1832, fought their first organized battle that year against the Mexican fort at Velasco, and in 1836, defeated a Mexican Army led by a skilled poker player—General Antonio López de Santa Anna—who had become Mexico's President.

Texas won her independence from Mexico in 1836, and became the Republic of Texas.

She sought admission to the United States, but was rejected. Texas then played a few side games with France and England, who seriously considered trying to add her to their stacks of chips. France was not then seated at the North American poker table, but she hadn't left the casino. England, of course, was still in the game.

In the wilderness of Texas were millions of

wild cattle and wild horses whose ancestors had escaped from Spanish and Mexican settlements long before. These animals, and the land itself, became blue chips.

The cattle started the Texas ranching industry. Before the railroads went west, the cows were slaughtered on the range for their hides and tallow. The hides were made into leather and the tallow into candles and soap in the growing industries of the American east coast and midwest. The meat was abandoned on the prairies, or sometimes thrown into convenient rivers. The Brazos River, said one Texas pioneer, had the best beef-fed fish in the world. Underneath the Texas soil were some buried aces. These included salt domes, petroleum, natural gas, and sulphur.

The United States for nearly ten years weighed the odds before annexing Texas. The hazardous risks involved in sectionalism and the slavery issue delayed the decision.

Another factor was the risk of war with Mexico.

In 1845, the United States backed her cards and annexed Texas. The show down with Mexico was not long in coming. The U. S. War with Mexico lasted from 1846 to 1848. By the terms of the treaty of peace, the United States gained Mexico's territory in the present limits of the United States (with the exception of a part of southern Arizona and New Mexico, which it acquired by the Gadsden Purchase of 1853) to the Pacific Ocean.

This included the present states of California, Nevada, Utah, and parts of Arizona, New Mexico, Colorado, and Wyoming.

The U. S. had also threatened war with England, over the Oregon territory, which both players claimed. Both had sent explorers, traders, and settlers to this area, which included Oregon, Washington, Idaho, parts of Montana, Wyoming, and about half of British Columbia. Both players had played several indecisive hands for the territory.

It was not until James K. Polk became U. S. President and the dealer that a player was able to make a bluff work and settle the issue. Polk, hoping to gain the southern half of the territory, threatened to take it all to the line of 54°40'. The American slogan was "Fifty-Four Forty or Fight!" The British offered to compromise at the 49th parallel. The United States in 1846 agreed to this compromise, and there was no fighting over the Oregon Territory.

The first chip to show its color in the new territories the United States won from Mexico was gold, in 1848, in California. The California Gold Rush began in 1849. The "Forty Niners" arrived by the Oregon Trail, by ships from Panama, by ships around Cape Horn, and by other trails across the country.

California's population increased by 40,000 in that year. In 1850, California became the first Pacific Coast state to enter the United States.

California was the 31st state to enter the United States. Since the time of the Louisiana Purchase in 1803, 13 other states had been populated and admitted to the Union. These included Louisiana, Indiana, Mississippi, Illinois, Alabama, Maine, Missouri, Arkansas, Michigan, Florida, Texas, Iowa, and Wisconsin.

Geography, geology, and the poker game had affected the development and settlement of all of these states. In Michigan, for example, the British had not surrendered Fort Detroit to the United States until 1796 — 13 years after the treaty which ended the American Revolution. Geology and geography had treated Michigan well. She had ports, furs, and timber, and also hidden cards, including salt brines, coal, iron, copper, and limestone.

Michigan joined the United States in 1837. She was for a number of years the leading salt-producing state. The salt brines were boiled with scrap lumber from the timber industry. Michigan salt helped Chicago become the great meat-packing center of the world. It captured the salt market from New York salt shipped by the Erie Canal.

Cincinnati, which often was called "Porkopolis" because of her packing companies, used salt from the Kanawha River Valley.

The salt brines available at Midland, Michigan were significant in the origin of The Dow Chemical Company.

Detroit put the world on wheels.

Even after the admission of California to the United States, there were notable gaps in the areas of settlement on the way to the newest state.

The first railroad routes to cross the west were surveyed before the American Civil War. The first line actually completed ran from Omaha, Nebraska, on the Missouri River, to San Francisco, and was finished in 1869.

In 1861, the Southern States wanted to split the U. S. chips and leave the game forever. Fortunately, they were brought back. But the years of the Civil War had delayed the development of the west — and the railroads.

The objective of the railroads, and other means of communication, was to tie the vast continental mass of the United States together.

When the railroads came westward, the nation's eating habits, and then the world's, began changing. The fabled Texas cattle drives to the railroads made beef available in almost any desired quantity. The cattle, gaunt and tough from their long travels, needed fattening before being made into beef. The cattle feeding industry began.

When railroads and ships introduced refrigeration, it was possible to ship fresh or frozen beef over the world. The refrigerant was brine — salt and water. [Ice cream makers also knew about salt and frozen water long before electric refrigeration was developed.] Omaha, Kansas City, and Chicago beefsteaks gained world fame. Michigan salt and Texas beef were in at the start of the fresh and frozen food distribution business.

The poker game has been long at the table marked "North America." From the first voyage of Columbus (1492) to the establishment of Jamestown, Virginia (1607), the game lasted for 115 years.

From the East Coast of North America to the Appalachian Mountains, the game continued for another 150 years.

From the Appalachians to the Mississippi, it was played for about 33 years, with some changes in the players.

From the Mississippi to the California coast, it took only 54 years. The gaps on the way to California were not filled up, in the pattern of statehood, for another 60 years. The United States, in the 1960's, expanded its frontiers further west to include Alaska and Hawaii.

The historian Frederic J. Turner likened the crossing of the continent to waves of frontiersmen, moving ever westward:

"The Atlantic frontier was compounded of fisherman, fur-trader, miner, cattle-raiser, and farmer. Excepting the fisherman, each type of industry was on the march toward the West, impelled by an irresistible attraction. Each passed in successive waves across the continent. Stand at Cumberland Gap and watch the procession of civilization, marching single file — the buffalo following the trail to the salt springs, the Indian, the fur trader and hunter, the cattle-raiser, the pioneer farmer — and the frontier has passed by. Stand at South Pass in the Rockies a century later and see the same procession with wider intervals between. The unequal rate of advance compels us to distinguish the frontier into the trader's frontier, the rancher's frontier, or the miner's frontier, and the farmer's frontier."

Turner might have added other frontiersmen who followed the farmer: the craftsman, the teacher, the doctor, the lawyer, the merchant, the engineer, the industrialist.

The poker game is not over yet. The players have changed, and a number of new games have been set up, but the United States is playing in most of them.

The American advances across the continent were not smooth and easy. They were costly in toil and blood — in death and disaster.

The native buffalo whose hoofs opened the frontier trails is gone.

The native Indians — that important non-European card in the original game — were consistent losers. It was never their frontier.

The continent was crossed at the expense of the Indians. Treaties and agreements were broken; terrible injustices were done. On the whole, the American Indians were probably treated no worse than many other native populations who fought back against the invasions of more technologically-advanced societies.

One of the most appropriate memorials to the American Indians was sent to Lord Dunmore, British Governor of Virginia (1774-76), as a message from Logan, a Mingo Indian chief who had been a friend of the whites.

(As there later arose controversy as to whether Logan accused the right person of the crime, the name is here made "Blank." The murder, and others, caused the Mingoes, the Shawnees, and the Delawares to go to war with Virginia. Virginia militia defeated them in a battle at the mouth of the Great Kanawha River. The Indians asked for peace.)

Logan would not attend the peace conference. He sent the message instead. Thomas Jefferson printed it as follows in the one book he wrote, *Notes on the State of Virginia:*

"I appeal to any white man to say, if ever he entered Logan's cabin hungry, and he gave him not meat; if ever he came cold and naked, and he clothed him not. During the course of the last long and bloody war, Logan remained idle in his cabin, an advocate for peace. Such was my love for the whites, that my countrymen pointed as they passed, and said, 'Logan is the friend of the white man.' I had even thought to have lived with you but for the injuries of one man. Col. Blank, the last spring, in cold blood, and unprovoked, murdered all the relations of Logan, not sparing even my women and children. There runs not a drop of my blood in the veins of any living creature. This called on me for revenge. I have sought it: I have killed many: I have fully glutted my vengeance. For my country, I rejoice at the beams of peace. But do not harbor a thought that mine is a joy of fear. Logan never felt fear. He will not turn on his heel to save his life. Who is there to mourn for Logan? — Not one."

—*William W. Boddie*

Salt and
The Lost Cause

In 1861, the economic, social, and political conflicts that had stirred, embittered, and divided the Northern and Southern sections of the United States of America for generations moved to the field of battle for settlement.

The South, which by then included parts of the present southwest, had developed on the pattern of Virginia, England's first American colony. Its economic base was the plantation system, and the use of black slaves to mass-produce cotton, tobacco, sugar cane, and rice. The South had achieved a monopoly in supplying cotton to the textile industries of New England and Europe. "Cotton is king!" the South said and believed.

The North, which by then included parts of the present Midwest and the Pacific Coast, had followed the pattern of Massachusetts, England's second American colony. It developed on a wide base of trade, commerce, fishing, shipping, finance, farming, mining, transportation, industry, and manufacturing.

When 11 Southern States seceded from the Union and established the Confederate States of America, they hoped that the North would let them separate peacefully. They intended to defend their new nation—they did not want to conquer the North.

Their political leaders were convinced that the North would not fight, and that if Northern armies were sent into the South, the Yankees would "cave-in" once Southern soldiers drove them out in defeat. They counted on the "Border States" of Kentucky, Missouri, and Maryland joining the Confederacy.

They believed that their cotton was an economic warfare weapon of such over-riding importance that the British and the French would be forced to send ships to Southern

Facing page: *At Fort Sumter, the Confederate cause began its march into history. Soon, Southern leaders were to become aware that supply shortages—including an acute lack of salt—were eroding the South's capabilities.*

ports for cotton in order to keep their textile mills operating. Thus the European nations could not only avoid the internal disorders resulting from great unemployment, but also continue to make money. Such a situation could lead to recognition of the Confederate States by the European powers and, perhaps, intervention to help the South.

All of these concepts, which shaped the fundamental political and military strategy of the Confederate Government, were wrong. The South therefore went to war without either a sound plan or the necessary resources to fight a long war and win it.

The South put an embargo on cotton. President Abraham Lincoln proclaimed a naval blockade of the South. He did not then have the ships to enforce it. But cotton piled up in the Confederacy, an almost wasted strategic asset. The British had stockpiled huge amounts. They were even able to export supplies to the New England cotton mills. By the time cotton did become scarce, Lincoln had many warships on station, enforcing the blockade of the South.

The cotton strategy backfired in another very important and unforeseen way. It cut off about one-half of the South's supply of salt. British ships coming for cotton and other trade had been bringing in enormous quantities of salt, even using it as ballast.

The Confederacy expected to continue securing salt from five other major sources then used by the South. They were the salt springs in the Goose Creek Valley near Manchester, Kentucky; the salt springs in the Great Kanawha River Valley near Charleston in western Virginia; the salt wells on the north fork of the Holston River at Saltville, Virginia; the salt wells near Mobile, Alabama; and a number of large salt licks, salt springs, and wells in northwestern Louisiana.

There was no salt mine known in either the South or the North in 1861. In all of the Southern States, there were some smaller brine sources, local in nature, and the South had a long seacoast where salt could be made from seawater.

Early in the war, the South began suffering for lack of salt. Most of the men were in the army. "What hogs we have to make our meat, we can't get salt to salt it," a Mississippi woman with sons in the army wrote the Governor of her state in 1861. The meat supplies for the army could not be preserved in the proper quantities, either.

The South relied more upon salted and brine-pickled meats than the North did for food for its soldiers and civilians. The South needed salt for making leather shoes, military equipment, and harness for horses and mules. While its demands for salt increased tremendously under the stresses of war, its supplies decreased drastically and rapidly.

In the wild political intrigues and military battles for the border states, the North beat out the South for Kentucky, Missouri, and Maryland.

The North took the Great Kanawha Valley saltworks in 1861. The Confederates regained them briefly in 1862 and then lost them permanently. Western Virginia (and four eastern Virginia counties) seceded from Virginia and joined the United States as the new state of West Virginia. The meat-packing plants of Cincinnati, Ohio, important to the North, depended upon Kanawha salt.

In 1862, the United States Navy came up the Mississippi from the Gulf of Mexico and forced its way past the Confederate forts guarding New Orleans. The capture of the city was one of the most strategic moves of the war. It closed the Mississippi to the South and was the first part of the North's plan to completely split off Louisiana, Texas, and Arkansas, and their resources, from the eight Confederate states east of the river. Meanwhile, a little-known General, U. S. Grant of the United States Army, had started fighting his way down the Mississippi and its tributaries toward Vicksburg, Mississippi.

Destiny could have taken a hand when, in 1862, the first rock salt mine in North America was discovered at Avery Island, near New Iberia, Louisiana. The solid salt came within 20 feet of the surface at Avery Island and could be mined directly, without boiling. It could have supplied the entire Confederacy. The United States forces made three attempts to take the saltworks. The Confederates, unable to provide an adequate defensive force, evacuated it in April, 1863, in advance of the third attempt.

On July 4, 1863, "Unconditional Surrender" Grant took Vicksburg and cut the last supply line between the eastern and western Confederate States. The same day, Confederate General Robert E. Lee began retreating from Gettysburg.

The Mississippi was open to the North; it was closed to the South.

The South was desperate for salt. Southern families, agencies of the Confederate Government, the states, counties, and towns swarmed to the seacoasts and to saline sources anywhere in the Confederacy to get or make their own supplies. The need was too big to be handled at the South's remaining large salt sources at Saltville, Mobile, and in northwestern Louisiana.

Salt was recognized by the North and the South as being as necessary as food itself. It was a factor of significance in the military operations of the armies of both.

The naval blockade was a powerful force in grinding the South down.

The blockade runners which brought the Confederacy munitions, medicine, and luxury goods, generally carried a few sacks, barrels, or packages of salt in their cargoes. They came for the Confederate cotton.

The real economic weapon of the war was not cotton but food, and closely allied with it was salt.

"Probably the most universally desired comfort of the Confederate soldier was something to eat," wrote Carlton McCarthy in recalling his war years as a member of the Confederate Army of Northern Virginia.

One day of marching and fighting without eating was common, he said; two days were "not uncommon," and there were times of three to four days.

Before the war ended, the Confederacy had developed resources enough to supply about 80 to 90 percent of the quantities of salt it had used in 1858-1860, when it had been supplying less than 20 percent of its own needs. These salt-works were frequently closed by Northern attacks. And even when the salt was produced, no adequate transportation system existed to distribute it.

The South continued to suffer from lack of planning—and from lack of salt. The North produced and imported plenty of salt during the war.

Saltville, which had been the best defended of the big Confederate salt sources, was still producing salt for the South when Lincoln, on March 9, 1864, made Grant commander of all United States Armies. On December 18-21, 1864, Saltville was raided and the works destroyed by Union forces.

Saltville was soon put back into service, but less than 4 months later, on April 9, 1865, Lee surrendered to Grant at Appomattox, Virginia. On April 12, Mobile surrendered. On May 26, the Confederate Army west of the Mississippi surrendered. The Confederacy had fallen. The cause of the South had been lost.

—William W. Boddie

The Salt Treasure of the Danakil

Modern man living in a developed nation of the Twentieth Century gives little thought to the salt that graces his table. It is the humblest of the staples in his diet. If ever he considers salt in the role of a trade commodity, he has little reason to give it any great monetary value.

Not so in the remote highlands of Ethiopia and the neighboring regions of Northeast Africa.

Here, in a trade that has varied but little in thousands of years, salt is a treasure with value approaching its weight in gold. Even the methods for obtaining the salt, and the very routes trod by men and animals in moving it from source to market, hark back to antiquity.

Ten thousand beasts of burden — camels, mules, donkeys — travel the ages-old trail from the Ethiopian highlands into the depths of the Danakil Depression. The trail is some 250 miles long, with altitude differences totalling 10,000 feet, An estimated 5,000 men make their livelihood in this trade, by mining table salt from the Danakil's inexhaustible reserves and transporting it to consumers in the highlands and beyond.

No one knows for certain when the first camels moved on this track. The trade was well established at the time of the very first Ethiopian empire, Aksum, which Third Century sources mention in the same breath with Rome, Persia, and China. For Aksum, the salt of the Danakil was one of the assets of empire.

Aksumitic trade expeditions exchanged salt for the gold, slaves, and ivory of the tribes dwelling on the southern and western frontiers of the empire. These goods then became Aksum's principal exports in its busy trade with Rome, Egypt, Syria, Arabia, and India.

The glory of Aksum has long since faded. But even today, in the remote regions of Ethiopia and throughout Northeast Africa, salt is as valuable as gold — and far better than money. Bricks of salt from the Danakil, in a single piece or sawn up to serve as low-denomination coins, pass readily from hand to hand in every market. They remain a form of hard currency unaffected by rate fluctuations.

The Danakil Depression, source of the salt, is a focal point of geological and scientific interest.

Prior pages: Strange and colorful formations abound on the Danakil Depression landscape. Some, like these, are produced when geysers bring metallic salts — compounds other than sodium chloride — from deep in the earth to harden on the surface.

Scientists visit and study the Danakil for what it can contribute to knowledge on the theory of continental drift. These studies, probing the processes that keep the earth's crust in perpetual motion and readjustment, were centered on the Danakil by a Belgian volcanologist, Haroun Tazieff. Most continental drift activity occurs on the beds of the oceans. Tazieff found that three rift zones meet in the Danakil, allowing study of the phenomena at close quarters and dryshod.

In appearance, the Danakil could be a world still in an early stage of geologic turmoil and evolution. The landscape consists of 120 miles of pure salt — sometimes monotonous and monochrome, but elsewhere bursting into a tumult of shapes and colors. There is expansive stillness with an intermingling of activity.

The salt plain dominates, of course. But here and there sulphurous springs pattern the desolation with networks of yellow veins. Warm, green-margined lakes lie in extinct craters. There are active volcanoes in whose maws the fires still smoulder. Fields of lava and seas of dunes are there. So are geysers, spewing steam and water. And where the hill of Dalol rises above the plain, yellow flowers of salt grow magically out of a green liquor — the chlorates of potassium and iron blossoming into unearthly gardens.

This is the strange, desolate and yet gaudy world of salt into which the caravans have come for centuries beyond memory. The journey, a six-day trek down and back, begins at Makale in the province of Tigre. The route crosses over high plains whipped by icy winds. It plunges down through woods of wild olives, past junipers and candelabra euphorbias into the realm of the mimosas and spreading acacias. And at last, after passing through meandering canyons, the caravan reaches the foot of the escarpment.

Now the trail is across the waterless plains. And finally across the crust of the fossil lake. Here the passage of the years has left virtually no mark other than the bleached animal skeletons along the way. Salt grates beneath the plodding feet of beast and man, salty perspiration burns the traveler's eyes, all through this endless and comfortless expanse.

Nor is there any great relief when the caravan reaches the site of the salt mining. Shade comes only in small rations. That created by tents of skins is reserved for the men who are producing the bricks of salt, and for the salt itself. For if the salt becomes too dry, it becomes brittle. And that must not be allowed.

The Afar, as the Danakil nomads call themselves, hold the traditional right to exploit the salt of their region. They have always jealously defended their right, by arms when necessary. And to supply their customer caravans, they move their settlements from time to time as they reach for better-quality salt on the expansive lake. Incidentally, their settlements are clusters of low huts built from blocks of salt.

Salt bricks are a product of teamwork, with a team of breakers working jointly with a number of hewers. The process begins when a small team uses sticks and metal bars to break large slabs out of the topmost layer of salt. Then, using axes, the slabs are broken into fragments a few square feet in area.

Now the hewers take over. They chop the fragments into bricks of uniform area and two standard thicknesses, known simply as thick and thin. This standardization, achieved by careful work with the adze, goes back to prehistoric times when no scales were available. It still simplifies marketing of the salt.

In dealing with the merchants in charge of the caravans, each production team of breakers and hewers acts as a collective. Deals between suppliers and transporters appear to be on a one-time basis, with no long-term or regular arrangements.

The standard lot of sale at the lake production point is 60 bricks of salt. The government-controlled price of a lot is three Ethiopian dollars—$1.20 in United States money. For the Afar salt worker, a day's work brings him about 1.50 Ethiopian dollars a day plus—also furnished by the salt buyer—his necessities of life, a daily loaf of bread and a goatskin of water.

Through the day while the salt bricks are being shaped, traded, and prepared for transport, the animals of the caravan wait patiently in the merciless sun. Camels, mules, and donkeys are well-fed for the work expected of them. Before they moved out into the salt plain, they were given all the fodder they had carried down from the highlands.

Now they are free for their loads of salt—and a long, hungry trek back to the mountains. Their drivers will walk beside them so as to use the full capacity of the caravan for the precious salt. Indeed, many a man will load a block of salt on his own shoulders.

Each camel will carry up to fifteen of the thick salt bricks; each mule, very little less. Mats will be used, not to protect the animals but to shield the loads from the baking heat of the sun. As far as possible, the caravans travel over the plains only when the sun is low. And under a full moon the string of caravans will flow without interruption all through the night so that, for any sleeper on the edge of a caravan trail, the clip-clop of the hooves weaves itself into a dream of the patter of summer rain.

Each salt caravan emerging from the Danakil must pass one fixed point, Berahle. This is a village on the border between the Christian highlands and the Moslem lowlands, not quite halfway along the return route and not quite halfway up the caravan's climb. Berahle is important as the point where the salt tax is levied.

Here each caravan moves in single file through a gate of sticks and thorns, reminiscent of passage through the famed Needle's Eye of the New Testament. As they pass, tax officials check the number and nature of all animals in the convoy and—irrespective of amount of salt in each load—collect a tax of three Ethiopian dollars for each camel, half as much for each mule, a fourth as much for each donkey. The tax receipt handed to the caravan driver becomes the passport for his trip to the market.

One lot of the thicker salt bricks, when it reaches the salt market of Makale, is worth up to $100 Ethiopian. Considering that the lot cost $3 Ethiopian, plus a little food and water, in the Danakil—and that the country's per capita annual income is less than $250 Ethiopian (or about $100 U.S.)—the salt trade might appear highly lucrative.

The reality is less rosy.

The salt tax, for instance, is an obvious expense. Others are the cost of food provided for animals and men, the rent paid for hired goatskins, the cost of ropes to secure loads. To hire an animal costs half the load he carries, plus the pay and food and accommodation expenses of any hired drivers. And while the journey takes only a week, each animal needs a month's rest for recovery if it is to survive the next trip.

The *ferengi*, the foreigner, is hard put to soundly assess the economics of this centuries-old trade. Why, for instance, should camels be used on the salt trails when a mule—cheaper

Following pages: Traveling a path centuries old, a caravan moves from the Ethiopian highlands toward the salt sources in the Danakil.

Top left: *Everything the caravan will need, including fodder for the animals, must be taken along on the trip to the salt.*

Bottom left: *The highlands and the hills are far behind, and the great salt flat is a burning desolation in the last long marches.*

Above: *The Afar, who live in the Danakil, have hereditary rights to produce the salt—and do so by methods almost as old as time.*

Left: Large slabs of salt pried from the lake bed by the breakers are then trimmed to standard sizes by the hewers.

Above: The salt blocks sold to the caravan merchants by the Afar are assembled into carefully-sized loads for the trip back.

Right: Every rope is made tight, every detail of the loading checked, to assure that the precious cargo of salt will get safely to market.

Following page: Men and animals swing into the marching stride of the caravan as, leaving the salt source, they head back to the highlands.

to buy and paying less tax—hauls nearly as much? The Ethiopian camel-driver shakes his head: "You would soon be bankrupt, *ferengi*. Don't you know that mules are as demanding as human beings, that they need a roof over their heads and daily food and water?"

So the salt caravans continue their journeys to and from the Danakil as they have from before the days of Aksum, little changed and little changing. There are temporary slow-downs, as in July and August when the streams of caravans thin down to a trickle. Or when the rainy season in the highlands causes flooding of the dried-out lake in the low plains. Or when the summer heat becomes so vicious as to drive out even the Afar.

Western-style progress, in the form of a good road and a few trucks, may some day reduce the caravan movement to a permanent trickle or end it entirely. Indeed, some years ago a road was in fact started in the direction of Dalol. But difficulties of terrain daunted the roadbuilders that the road petered out in the mountains.

Rather than push the road project, the Prince of Makale, Governor-General of the province of Tigre, decided to improve the caravan route. At several particularly arduous passages on the escarpment, bulldozers carved out zig-zag paths—and substantially increased the salt transport capacity.

The old bottlenecks were particularly danger-ous congestion points when caravan traffic was moving in both directions. With scant room for passing on the then-narrow trails, animals sometimes fell to their deaths or loads of salt bricks were broken against rock walls or in collisions. Today the animals streaming in opposite directions can pass one another with ease, though still closely enough for a highland-bound camel to snatch an occasional mouthful of hay from a bundle being carried plainsward by a distant relation.

But that widening of the caravan trail, plus the now-and-then appearance of a motor vehicle, and a few scientists studying rift structures or geologists probing the Danakil's unknowns in the region of Dalol, are almost all that has changed on Ethiopia's salt trail over the centuries. For the people of Northeast Africa, just as for Europe in the bronze and iron ages, salt is still a treasure worthy of great and tortuous exertion and toil.

The Troubled Future of the Imperial Valley

The Imperial Valley, in the southeast corner of California, is one of the world's richest and most diversified agricultural areas. On less than a half-million acres, the Imperial Valley in 1970 produced crops and livestock with an on-the-farm value of some $257 million.

And every acre, as well as every dollar of yield, is directly dependent on irrigation.

True, the Imperial Valley is blessed with almost incredibly rich soils. In a long-ago geological era the valley was an extension of the Gulf of California and the bed of the Colorado River. For centuries the river deposited its burden of silt here as it approached the sea. Then some great upheaval sealed off the valley, put the Colorado into a new course, and the valley — with a soil depth as great as one mile in some places — dried out.

When the gold-seekers trekked through the region in the Great California Gold Rush of 1849, many of the farmers among them recognized the richess of the soil. But rich or not, they saw it then as rich soil in a stretch of desert just as barren as the unproductive lands that still surround the Imperial Valley.

Some among those early visitors must have envisioned the valley as it could be with an assured water supply. For in the next half-century a long series of legal, technical, financial, political, and organizational efforts — often marked by struggle, conflict, and opposition — sought to bring water to that promising but thirsty land.

This was finally accomplished in 1901. And once achieved, the introduction of irrigation water set in motion two series of events.

Facing page: *Agriculture on the scale and complexity seen in the Imperial Valley is an extensive, fast-moving enterprise — as reflected in the controlled intensity of activity in this packing shed where tomatoes are being processed.*

One has been the development of the Imperial Valley as both an irrigation miracle and a veritable agricultural treasure trove.

The second has been a succession of severe troubles, each constituting a threat with the potential for ending the valley's richness forever.

Irrigation of the valley began in 1901. Water was taken from the Colorado River, with a pumping station at Yuma and the old, dried-up bed of the Alamo River as the main feeder canal. This 60-mile route lay partly in Mexican territory.

Availability of water brought an unprecedented boom. By 1904, about 12,000 people had settled in the valley. They built some 700 miles of canals to distribute the water over the 77,000 acres they put to the plow. And they quickly established the Imperial Valley as a thriving grain and dairy producing area.

Today there are more than 3,000 miles of canals in the network irrigating the Imperial Valley. The 437,000 acres now watered to abundant vitality yield an all but incredible variety of foods.

The "crop" bringing the greatest dollar volume, for example, is animals for slaughter— principally beef cattle. These come to the feed yards of the valley from southeastern California, from neighboring states, and from Mexico for pre-market finishing on the lush graze.

Field crops range from anise to zucchini. Among these there are more than 30—varieties of vegetables, melons, and forage crops—whose market value tops $1 million each year.

Largest, and most valuable, of the vegetable crops from the Imperial Valley is head lettuce. During the winter months of December, January, and February, head lettuce from the valley enjoys an unsurpassed market position. Two trains a day carry the lettuce to waiting markets —100 carloads, enough to provide 90 percent of America's salads.

There is no magic to this development of extensive farm production through irrigation. Prudence, organization, and technical know-how have been the key ingredients. Plus, the record shows, a willingness to face up to near-disaster—and courage to overcome great difficulties.

The first settlers and farmers, for instance, did not reckon on the burden of sediment carried along in the Colorado River waters. In each acre foot of water (an acre foot being enough water to cover an acre to a depth of one foot), the river brought 10 tons of silt into the irrigation system.

Some of this silt settled out of the water and gradually built up along the bottoms of the canals and ditches. Much more serious trouble came in 1904 when the silt plugged up the pumping station, stopping the irrigation flow to the valley farms.

To save their crops the settlers cut a temporary opening at a new location so as to once again bring water to their fields. They were, unknowingly, inviting disaster.

In four violent waves the Colorado River lurched through this breach, overran the canal, and began pouring its entire flow into the Imperial Valley. Wide expanses were under water. The river began digging a new bed up to a quarter-mile wide. It ran its course to the deepest spot in the depression, a low-lying salt marsh which the river filled and transformed into the present day Salton Sea.

Now began a desperate, night-and-day struggle to lock the Colorado back into its prior course. It took 18 months to achieve. To construct the dam and dike that finally choked off the flow, Indians—Pima, Papago, Maricopa, Yuma— wove huge mats to be set into the breach. Against and around the mats, tons of rock were hauled in and dumped in an around-the-clock operation given the entire resources of the Southern Pacific Railway. At last, in 1907, the effort succeeded in returning the Colorado to its original bed.

A significant result of the flood catastrophe was the founding of the Imperial Irrigation District. This authority, organized under the California water law, was assigned responsibility for operating and maintaining all water supply and distribution facilities for the valley. Its first great task was directing the recovery from the flood.

But the great blossoming of the Imperial Valley, and full development of the present irrigation complex, had to await some major control structures on the Colorado. The first was Hoover Dam where, in 1935, the formation of Lake Mead began as the dam began backing up the river's water.

Hoover Dam ended the danger of destructive floods on the lower Colorado. Lake Mead, holding in reserve twice the average annual flow of the river, guarantees a supply of irrigation water—and one that can be regulated as needed.

Then in 1938 the Imperial Dam was completed.

This is a diversionary project with silt sedimentation pools. Here the river water destined for the Imperial Valley is slowed down in its flow, so that the silt has a chance to settle out before it can clog the irrigation works. Then, by way of the All-American Canal—a delivery route that does not touch Mexico—the Imperial Dam sends the Colorado water to the valley.

The Imperial Valley irrigation complex has more than its 3,000 miles of canals among its notable features. For instance, the entire system operates by gravity flow. Water enters the system at a weir 181 feet above sea level; water leaving the system goes to the Salton Sea, which is 231 feet below sea level.

Another unusual feature is the highly organized, smoothly working distribution operation—so effective that customers rank the District as the world's best irrigation water supplier. The farmer who wants water simply puts in an order and gets delivery. He can place his order in person at the El Centro headquarters of the District, or by letter or telephone. And within 72 hours the water he ordered is flowing onto the acreage he wants to have irrigated.

Some 2.7 million acre feet of water were handled by the District just that way in 1970. And the farmers who got it also appreciated the comparatively low price involved. The 1970 cost of an acre foot of water, delivered, was only $2.30.

All in all, the facts and figures about the Imperial Valley are so impressive as to create a picture of man triumphant over a barren desert, over early error, over a raging river. And so it is—so far. For nature is again threatening the Imperial Valley.

And the weapon nature is using is salt.

The Colorado River in its natural state contains more dissolved salts than do most other rivers. Many of these salts are washed into the Colorado from the barren wastelands of its drainage area.

Man and his works add to the river's natural salt content. Upstream of the Imperial Dam, for instance, there are other irrigated areas which send their drain waters—heavily salt-laden—into the Colorado. And in the reservoir at Lake Mead, evaporation from the lake surface has the effect of concentrating the salt content of the water.

The net effect of these and other factors is considerable. From 1953 to 1970, the salt content in irrigation water flowing in the All-American Canal increased by 35 percent or more. The present-day salt load works out to be 1.27 tons per acre foot. Putting it another way: A 160-acre cotton field in the Imperial Valley, getting a total depth of eight feet of irrigation water during the growing season, will also receive 1,600 tons of salt from the Colorado.

That's a mountain of salt. And it's expected to be even greater in coming years as more upstream acreage is brought under irrigation.

Another point adds to the severity of this salt problem. The highest level of salinity of the Colorado River comes at the very time when Imperial Valley winter crops are germinating. And seed of virtually all types is especially sensitive to damage by salt.

But as some slight balance, there is one point of consolation for the farmers in the Imperial Valley. The salts that the Colorado River brings to their fields are types that are relatively easy to dissolve. So they tend to leach out of the soil, particularly if salt-free or low-salt water is applied.

The growers and ranchers of the Imperial Valley, however, remain confident in spite of the salt menace. They know that the valley, in its short history, has heard a number of Jeremiahs whose predictions of doom have never been fulfilled. One gloomy theory, for instance, says that the Hoover Dam takes so much sediment out of the Colorado that the river's delta is being eroded by the ocean waves—which will enable the ocean to reclaim the entire trough that includes the Imperial Valley. Another theory holds that disaster will come from too much sediment—that an overload on the Colorado delta will cause it to sink, thus letting in the sea. There are more such warnings of doom. None of them wins great attention.

Still, the message which salt is writing on the fields is not being overlooked. A battle, more technical and subtle and thus less openly dramatic than the fight against sediment and flood in 1904-1907, is being waged against the salt. The growers and ranchers, while fully aware that the valley's future demands water quality as well as quantity, feel that they have time for successful action.

H. M. "Red" Sperber, a graduate agronomist and member of the County Board of Supervisors, says: "No doubt, we have got ourselves a problem here, a real problem. We need lots of tiling, more drainage ditches, new farming techniques to overcome it. But to go out of business? Never! Not, at least, before the year 2000."

Most of the farmers seem to share Sperber's

Above: These extensive control structures at the Imperial Dam slow the flow of Colorado River water so that much of the load of sediment is settled out before the water is channeled on for irrigation use.

Left: Melons by the truckload come from the irrigated fields of the Imperial Valley. They represent just one of the more than 30 crops with an annual market value of over $1 million which the region produces.

Facing page, left: Unglamorous, perhaps, but the onion has a high place among Imperial Valley crops. These are going to market in a season when the Valley is virtually the nation's sole source.

Facing page, right: Where the land—given water—yields abundantly, there must be means for harvesting the crop quickly, efficiently, thoroughly. Machines of special design are here used to gather carrots in the fields of the Imperial Valley.

view. And they are not alone in their efforts to solve the salt problem. The Imperial Irrigation District is highly conscious of the salt threat — and active in reducing it. So is the Soil Conservation Service of the U. S. Department of Agriculture, other government agencies, and more than one privately supported research group. Their several efforts add up to a broad approach involving and testing multiple possibilities. Those that prove helpful are getting application.

The District, for instance, lines the major water distribution canals with concrete. This prevents irrigation water from seeping out and depositing salt on low-lying land alongside the canals. Where concrete is uneconomical, interceptor conduits are buried parallel to canals — to catch seepage water and return it to the canal.

In addition, the District allows farmers to buy water above their irrigation needs. This water, requiring no special permit, can be used to flood fallow acreages so as to wash out — or leach — some or all of the salt the land is holding.

The Soil Conservation Service strongly promotes improved drainage as a primary precautionary measure against the salt buildup. Improvements range from deep plowing techniques to the use of plastic tubing, rather than tile or concrete, for drains.

Deep plowing encourages better drainage by breaking up layers of soil otherwise impenetrable to water. Plastic drainage tubing is cheaper, longer lasting, faster to install, and less subject to damage or dislocation in farm operations than is concrete or tile.

These efforts are showing some positive results. Since 1949 the Imperial Valley has consistently sent more salt into the Salton Sea than has been brought in by the All-American Canal. Measurements made every week show, for example, that the 1961 excess of salt drained out over salt taken in was 358,000 tons.

Such statistics are encouraging. But these salt riddance values must be seen in proper perspective. After all, a farmer who leaches the salt from 100 acres improves the statistical average for every acre.

Wayne Flanagan, Chief of the SCS for the District, puts it this way: "Average values must not dazzle us. We are dealing with individual parcels of land and, looked at this way, we are losing ground. Every two weeks a different farmer reports trouble. Last year a certain piece of land was still good; now, nothing seems to want to grow on it, not even cotton or barley. The salt caught up with it."

Expectably, several factors figure in the loss of once-fertile fields to the intruder. The network of buried drains is vital to ridding the fields of water fast enough so that the salt won't stay in the soil. But even with some 17,000 miles of drains in place, SCS experts consider another 17,000 miles are needed. And these drains are expensive. In some places, where the heavier and denser soils less permeable to water are being cultivated, drain lines in the network are only 25 feet apart. If the prospective cost of drainage would make a field unprofitable, the farmer may abandon poorer acreages to the salt.

Another factor is absentee ownership. About 60 percent of Imperial Valley land is owned by people who live elsewhere. Some absentee owners tend to ignore warnings of salt danger until they can find no more tenants for their land — and that's often too late to head off the trouble. To discourage this, more and more of the region's banks are requiring that any land on which they loan money have a functioning drainage system in place.

But all these measures, and even experiments to find and develop crops with high tolerance to salt, are only partial answers. What the Imperial Valley really needs is lots and lots of surplus water, preferably salt-free, to spread over the fields in a long-range washing action to clear out the salt.

Where's the water going to come from?

One suggestion is to get an added million acre feet by clearing the Colorado River and all the canals of the vegetation that consumes water and also increases evaporation loss by slowing the flow. The Imperial Irrigation District already pursues a superior, year-around herbicide control program to keep main canals and laterals clear and free-flowing.

Now the District is experimenting with a species of perch, *Tilapia mossambica*, imported from Africa. The *Tilapia* have an insatiable appetite for moss and water plants. So far, they are multiplying and working well in the experiment.

Another suggestion is that the Colorado River be channelized — have its bed straightened and cleared of all water plants. Environmentalists oppose this, and question whether the estimated saving of a million acre feet of water a year is worthwhile.

The question is valid—because to effectively protect the Imperial Valley against salinization would require from 4 to 9 million acre feet of additional water. Some exotic sources have been suggested. Among them:

• Modification of the weather, to get more salt-free rainfall for the valley.

• Desalinization of sea water and delivery of the fresh water output to the irrigation system.

• Tapping the Columbia River, although studies on such a gigantic project would require at least 30 years—and are prohibited from consideration until at least 1978 by terms of an existing water agreement.

• Development and application of geothermal energy.

This last presents a hope for the immediate future. It is based on a boiler that nature has buried deep beneath the Imperial Valley, and on successful development in Mexico of steam wells that tap underground reserves of natural steam.

Most significantly, the Mexican geothermal energy field of Cerro Prieto, in Mexicali, lies in the southern continuation of the Imperial Valley. Wells drilled at Cerro Prieto yield an average of 500 tons of steam and hot water an hour. And since the early 1960's, drilling of similar steam wells has been in progress around the Salton Sea.

Experts consider it possible that the most important source of natural steam in the United States lies below the Imperial Valley. If so, the farmers and ranchers of the valley know how they want this resource put to service. They envision multi-purpose units drawing steam from deep-lying pockets of volcanic heat to yield both fresh water and energy. The energy could then be applied to produce fresh water from sea water, and deliver it to the valley at a price low enough to permit refilling and cleansing the Colorado.

Perhaps this sounds like a grandiose dream. But then, the Imperial Valley—as agricultural treasure house, as complex irrigation demonstration, as an area exposed to potential economic disaster—is hardly less than grandiose. And so, in overall aspect, is the fight being waged against the intruding salt.

Dow and Salt's Advancing Frontiers

Salt, which has exerted such powerful in-fluences upon man's societies and institutions, was one of the compelling necessities of exist-ence that determined the distribution pattern of mankind on earth.

Around the world, where salt was available in plenty or could be obtained by trade, early societies and civilizations grew. Where salt was constantly in short supply, societies were slower in developing.

Early man was a prisoner of his dietary needs. When he ventured into new territories, he could find salt by following animal trails. Salt had an irresistible attraction for animals, and for man.

Man quickly recognized a value in salt beyond the taste itself: salt would lure animals into his ambush and not only provide him with food, but also with the means of preserving the surplus meat and the skins, thanks to the same salt that attracted them both.

Battles and wars were fought for possession of salt sources. When a salt source was once discovered, it was not forgotten, regardless of its ownership. It continued to be used by gen-eration after generation and by society after society.

The animal paths became trails, caravan routes, and roads.

Thus, civilization followed the routes to salt. For untold centuries, man had to stay within range of salt. Salt was essential—salt was life itself.

Man experimented with salt, as he did with other resources he found in his environment or that he could secure by trade. He knew that salt had secrets. But he was able to learn only a few of them.

The key to unlocking salt's secrets, and chang-ing and expanding the nature of salt's role in civilization, was industrial chemistry. Indus-trial chemistry began evolving from the mists of alchemy and superstitions in the latter half of the 1700's.

For more than 100 years, salt was the heart of the industrial chemical development.

Consequently, salt again exerted powerful influences upon the locations, the research and development work, and the operations of the chemical industry in its early formative period.

There are countless names involved in salt-based chemistry in such roles as theorists, discoverers, inventors, technologists, and manufacturers. Three names, however, stand out preeminently. They are Leblanc, Solvay, and Dow.

It was the need for securing an additional source of alkali that led the French physician Nicolas Leblanc to develop a method of producing it from salt in 1787. Alkali, needed in the manufacture of textiles, dyes, soap and glass, had been supplied from the most ancient of times mainly from the ashes of trees and seaweed in the form of "potash." A few natural deposits of alkali (sodium carbonate) also were known to exist. These sources were now inadequate.

Leblanc treated salt with sulphuric acid (discovered in the early 1600's) and roasted the resulting salt cake (sodium sulphate) with limestone and coal. Sodium carbonate, the desired alkali, was extracted from the black ash with water. The water was boiled off.

Coincidentally, France's increased alkali needs were caused by her wars preceding and incident to the French Revolution (1789). This revolution, so significant in western civilization, was caused in part by abuses of the *gabelle*, or salt tax, by the French royalty and privileged classes.

Leblanc was the first person to change salt into a new and more beneficial form in a large-scale industrial process. He opened wider horizons for salt and for chemistry.

Leblanc's soda process released hydrochloric acid gas. The problem was solved in time by absorbing the gas in water and turning it to a beneficial use as a bleaching agent for textiles. Traditionally, textile manufacturers bleached new cloth by treating it with buttermilk and exposing the cloth to the sun for several months in bleach fields.

The next to significantly advance the technology of industrial salt chemistry were two Belgian brothers, Albert and Ernest Solvay.

They developed an entirely new process which produced soda more economically than the Leblanc process. The raw materials were salt, water, limestone, and coal. The Solvay process, a continuous one, was also called the ammonia-soda process because of the nature of the chemistry involved.

The Solvays built a plant and had it successfully operating by 1867. Despite many improvements made by manufacturers using the Leblanc method, they could not compete with the more efficient ammonia-soda process.

The Solvay process gradually replaced the previous one and still supplies a large part of the world's alkali needs. The company that the brothers founded has expanded into many other areas of activity.

During the past century, scientific knowledge increased enormously. In chemistry, the three particularly-important steps forward are considered to be the ammonia-soda process, the development of synthetic (man-made) organic chemicals, and electrochemistry.

Herbert H. Dow, an 1888 graduate in chemistry of Case School of Applied Science (now Case Western Reserve University), was one of the outstanding pioneers of electrochemistry. He had become interested in brines and their salt contents while he was in his last year in the Cleveland, Ohio, school. In 1889, he developed and patented a new process for removing bromine from brine.

Dow's destiny was in the brines that lay underneath Midland, Michigan. It took him nine years and several starts before he organized and set The Dow Chemical Company successfully on its upward climb in 1897.

Dow was not the first to use the Midland salt source. Thousands of years previously, the Sauk Indians were using it. Under the pressure of the European colonizers on the North American east coast, the Chippewas had moved westward and driven the Sauks out. French trappers and fur traders, and later the British, traded with the Chippewas. When the first American surveyors moved through central Michigan in 1837, they noted that the settlement of Midland, on the Tittabawassee River and nearby salt springs, had been "located" but at that time had no inhabitants.

The timber industry was the next user of the brine; and a salt industry developed in which the waste timber was utilized to boil out the salt from the brine.

The salt producers were followed by the bromine producers. The Midland brine contained bromine. This was an undesirable impurity to producers of common salt (sodium chloride) but a desirable product for the pharmaceutical industry.

Midland was, when Dow first saw it, the leading bromine producing center in the United States. The producers pumped brine from wells into large kettles. The brine was heated until the common salt precipitated. This salt was removed and the remaining liquor was treated with an oxidant and an acid (generally sulphuric acid) and heated until the bromine evaporated into a collection system.

In a somewhat parallel situation to that of the Solvays, Dow had a new process which made the process then employed obsolete. He passed an electric current through cold brine. This caused the brine to release the bromine. He blew air through the brine to vaporize the bromine and direct it to a collection system.

Dow's first generation products were bromine-based. His second generation were chlorine-based. His third generation products were based on the magnesium chloride and calcium chloride salts that were also parts of the Midland brine. Further along, his organization worked with iodine salts in brine and developed and used processes to mine the sea itself for bromine and magnesium.

Dow used the same brines that his predecessors had used. However, through the development and application of technology he originated an organization which has, in the 75 years of its existence, probably used more component parts of salts to manufacture more beneficial products for society than mankind has done in previous history.

However, Dow's pathways have been more closely interlinked with products that could be made from a start in common salt than with any other single material. Dow's key to salt was the separation, by electrochemistry, of the chlorine and the sodium components of this salt.

These components were then used in combinations with other materials to produce new chemicals, upgraded in value to society. Often the new chemicals were especially-designed for tasks that needed to be done.

The Dow organization constantly studied salt and new ways to employ it. It became the world's largest producer of chlorine. It is also one of the world's largest producers of caustic soda, an alkali produced as a co-product of the chlorine.

Historically, Dow has utilized most of its chlorine inside its own plants. When Dow began combining chlorine with petroleum raw materials — particularly with ethylene — a vast profusion of products resulted. Dow now produces more than 1,100 products. About 80 percent use chlorine or caustic soda in some way in the course of their manufacture.

When Dow expanded beyond its location in Midland, Michigan, it went to places where salt was available, just as civilization had done.

The first such move was to Pittsburg, California, in 1938. The salt Dow uses there is produced by solar evaporation from the waters of San Francisco Bay.

The second move was to Freeport, Texas, in 1940. The salt that attracted Dow there was in great underground dome foundations. It was there that Dow mined the ocean for magnesium and bromine. It was there too that Dow's marriage of salt and ethylene resulted in the growth of one of the world's largest chemical complexes.

The third move was to Sarnia, Ontario, in 1942. Again, salt was there. The fourth, to Plaquemine, Louisiana — salt and ethylene, in 1956.

In the fifth major move, Dow went to Europe and in 1964, close to the scenes where salt played major roles in the civilization of the Middle Ages, began building a large chemical complex at Terneuzen, The Netherlands. Within range are ethylene and salt — the salt unused as yet, but this will not always be so.

In 1972, Dow went on stream with a new manufacturing complex at Stade, Germany. Stade was one of the Hanseatic League cities that traded salt and other essential articles in the Middle Ages. Near Stade, unknown then, is a large underground salt formation.

In Latin America, Dow has manufacturing plants in Mexico, Colombia, Brazil, Argentina, and Chile. Salt is the base of much of their production.

In the Pacific area, Dow has a major manufacturing plant in Australia (salt is involved) and a major joint venture, Asahi-Dow Limited, in Japan. Asahi-Dow, the oldest of Dow's joint venture companies, was founded in 1952 to produce Dow's saran fiber, whose raw materials are salt and ethylene. Other Dow joint ventures are located in Korea, Australia, New Zealand, Malaysia, and India.

In the United States, Dow has manufacturing plants in more than 20 states. Salt is often a starting raw material, or eventually will become one.

In Europe, in addition to Holland and Germany, Dow has manufacturing plants in Great Britain, France, Italy, and Greece. Dow-Unquinesa, formed in 1960 in Spain, has a salt base.

Salt has taken Dow, as it has taken civilization, into many places and into many activities. Products made in part from salt fulfill the needs of most phases of today's society.

Wherever you look, you see around you materials and goods which Dow and salt made possible.

Have salt's secrets all been unlocked? Hardly. Dr. Dow, who originated this company in 1897, would be gratified to learn that a Dow epoxy resin served as the heat shield on the Apollo spacecraft that took American astronauts to the moon — but he would not have been surprised to learn that common salt was a starting material.

What is salt's future? Its future is unknown and unpredictable. But this mysterious necessity has maintained and vastly increased its role in human affairs since industrial chemistry gave it the means to perform tasks undreamed of in 1897 — the year The Dow Chemical Company was born.

— *William W. Boddie*